PENGUIN

THE LAZY CONMAN AND OTHER STORIES

A writer based in Kathmandu, Ajit Baral has contributed to numerous magazines and newspapers within and outside Nepal. He co-edited *New Nepal, New Voices*, an anthology of Nepali short stories in English. He edits *Read*, a magazine, and helps run Fine Print, a publishing house in Nepal. He also coordinates the literary page for *Dainiki*, a Nepali daily. A collection of his interviews of international writers, *Interviews across Time and Space*, was published in 2007.

THE
LAZY CONMAN
AND OTHER STORIES

{FOLKTALES FROM NEPAL}

AJIT BARAL

ILLUSTRATIONS BY
DURGA BARAL

PENGUIN BOOKS

PENGUIN BOOKS
Published by the Penguin Group
Penguin Books India Pvt. Ltd, 7th Floor, Infinity Tower C, DLF Cyber City,
Gurgaon 122 002, Haryana, India
Penguin Group (USA) Inc., 375 Hudson Street, New York, New York 10014, USA
Penguin Group (Canada), 90 Eglinton Avenue East, Suite 700, Toronto, Ontario,
M4P 2Y3, Canada
Penguin Books Ltd, 80 Strand, London WC2R 0RL, England
Penguin Ireland, 25 St Stephen's Green, Dublin 2, Ireland (a division of Penguin
Books Ltd)
Penguin Group (Australia), 707 Collins Street, Melbourne, Victoria 3008, Australia
Penguin Group (NZ), 67 Apollo Drive, Rosedale, Auckland 0632, New Zealand
Penguin Books (South Africa) (Pty) Ltd, Block D, Rosebank Office Park, 181 Jan
Smuts Avenue, Parktown North, Johannesburg 2193, South Africa

Penguin Books Ltd, Registered Offices: 80 Strand, London WC2R 0RL, England

First published by Penguin Books India 2009

Copyright © Ajit Baral 2009

Illustrations © Durga Baral 2009

All rights reserved

10 9 8 7 6 5 4 3 2

ISBN 9780143103868

Typeset in Perpetua by Eleven Arts, New Delhi
Printed at Repro India Ltd, Navi Mumbai

A PENGUIN RANDOM HOUSE COMPANY

Contents

Introduction

When I was a child, my eldest brother used to tell me stories of ghosts and demons to put me to sleep. He would point at the lights flickering on the hill across our house and tell me that they were *ranke bhuts*, flaming ghosts who walk the night. Today I have forgotten most of the stories that he used to tell me but I am sure some of them were folktales that he had heard from elders, suitably embellished and modified with details that he thought would best scare me. And just as these stories that were handed down as part of an oral tradition have passed out of my recollection, they have also slowly faded from the collective consciousness.

Folktales enjoyed wide circulation and popularity in Nepal because they were one of the few means of recreation. We've all heard apocryphal tales of how mothers used to feed recalcitrant children: when, awed by the stories they were hearing, children opened their mouths wide, their mothers quickly spooned food into their mouths. Nepal's economy has always been primarily agrarian and many of its folktales are connected to, and shaped by, agricultural activities. They served to pass time when shepherds had to watch over flocks at night or when on the grazing grounds in the day. Folktales were also excellent vehicles for lessons on good values, morality and ethics.

However, with time, other distractions like radio, television, films, and, later, video games came in and people, especially children, quickly took to them. These developments coincided with changes in the societal sphere. Both men and women started to take up varied professions and nuclear families became the norm. As life changed gears and became faster, there was less and less time for storytelling. It is little wonder, therefore, that folktales and the art of narrating stories has all but vanished in the urban spheres of our life. Rural life, too, which was once the fertile soil from which these folktales sprang, has changed. More and more people are migrating to the cities from villages; people in the cities are migrating out of the country, and the pervasive reach of modern forms of entertainment has not left villages untouched. It is important that we preserve these stories which are such an important part of our heritage so that the generations yet to come can enjoy them.

In 1940, a collection of folktales, *Nepali Dantekatha*, by Bodh Bikram Adhikari appeared. A few years later, the Nepali Bhasa Prakashani Samiti started to explore and collect folktales from different parts of the country. *Dantekatha Mala* by Lalitjang Sijapati appeared in 1947 and *Danthekatha* by Subarna Shamsher in 1949. A few collections appeared in the next decade but the most exhaustive of them, perhaps till date, appeared in 1975. It was edited by folklorist Tulsi Diwas and published by the then Royal Nepal Academy. If very few collections of folktales have appeared in Nepali, fewer still have appeared in English, and only recently. Some of these include *Tales of Kathmandu* by Karna Sakya and Linda Griffith, *Nepali Folk Stories and Legends* by Karunakar Vaidya and *The Seven Sisters and Other Nepali Tales* by Kesar Lal. *The Lazy Conman and Other Stories* is an addition to this body of work already in existence. I do hope that these stories which, though simple, tell us much about ourselves, illustrated by one of Nepal's foremost cartoonists, will appeal to both the young and the old.

Ajit Baral

The Lazy Conman
and Other Stories

Folktales from Nepal

The Lazy Conman

There once lived a couple in a village in the mountains of Nepal. They were very poor and the husband was a very lazy man. He would sit at home all day, warming himself in the sun on days when it was out and in front of the kitchen fire on days it wasn't. His wife did all the work in the fields and at home. She would fetch firewood from the forest and drinking water from the springs. One day, just as she was entering the house lugging a heavy *gagri*, a vessel, of water, her husband asked her for a cup of tea. This was unbearable. She shouted, 'What sort of a man are you? You sit at home all day doing nothing, while I unceasingly labour. If you had any sense, any self respect at all, you would help me out in the fields and then we could have a little money.' The husband was incensed: how dare she speak to him in this manner? He yelled at her, 'I do nothing because I can make a fortune without even half trying.' His wife snorted in contempt, 'Empty talk is easy, husband.' The man angrily stomped off.

In a towering rage, he walked very fast for a while. But

as soon as he was out of sight, he slowed down. His shoes were old and in a state of disrepair; they began to hurt his feet. He hobbled on for a while and reached a village. There he stopped a passer-by and asked if any cobbler plied his trade in the village. The passer-by directed him to one. When his shoe was mended, the man asked, 'How much?'

The cobbler replied, 'A paisa.'

Pointing to a sweet-shop in the distance, he told the cobbler, 'The owner of that sweet-shop there will give you the money.'

He then put on his newly-repaired shoe and went to the sweet-shop. There he asked for sweets worth a paisa. When the sweets were handed over, the man pointed at the cobbler who was coming towards the sweet-shop and said, 'The cobbler there will give you the money.' When the cobbler arrived within earshot, the man said, without looking at anyone in particular, 'A paisa, right?' Both the cobbler and the shop-owner assumed the other was being addressed and in the confusion, the man quickly walked away.

He walked for a while before coming to a spring where some *dhobi* women were washing clothes. Some children were playing nearby. He walked up to the children and finding a level spot, spread his tattered handkerchief and putting the sweets on it, proceeded to eat them in full view. The children eyed him for some time and then coming up to him, asked for a taste. When he refused, they ran to their mothers and began to pester them. One of the washerwomen walked up to the man and requested him to give the children some sweets. He spun for her a tale of great hunger and deprivation: he could not share the sweets with the children because that would mean starvation for him. However, he did know that in the nearby village, the sweet-shop owner was giving sweets away for free. He had got his sweets from there. The washerwomen all rushed off, children in tow. The man calmly tied up the clothes they had left behind into a bundle and stuffing the bundle into a bucket, quit the scene. He walked very fast and when he was sure that the women could not find him, stopped at a beautiful meadow. There he decided to rest and eat the sweets still left with him. After his meal, he looked for a medium-sized tree and climbing it, draped the branches with the clothes. He then filled the bucket with water and sat down to wait.

Soon, he saw a man at the top of the road. He hurriedly got up and began to water the tree, singing loudly and making a great show of the exercise. He was lucky; the man was a merchant. The merchant asked the man, 'Brother, what are you doing?'

The man replied, pretending irritation, 'Do you not have eyes? Can't you see that I am watering my tree?'

The merchant said, 'But there are clothes on the branches.'

'Yes, I would expect a clothes-tree to grow clothes—wouldn't you?'

The merchant was intrigued; he saw great profit here. He asked the man to sell him the tree. The man refused outright but the merchant kept upping his bid. When he quoted two thousand silver coins for the tree, the man relented but put forward a condition: he would get to keep all the clothes the tree had already borne. However, he would throw in the bucket for free. When the merchant agreed, he tied up the clothes into a bundle and pocketing the money, walked on.

He came across a dancing bear that had escaped from its handler. The man caught the animal and leashed it to a stake on open ground. He then waited for a suitable victim.

As soon as he spotted someone in the distance, he stuffed some of the silver coins up the bear's rectum and began driving it round the stake. The passer-by was another merchant on his way to the city. It seemed odd that this man should give a performance with a dancing bear in the middle of nowhere. He asked the man, 'Brother, what are you doing?'

The man replied, without preamble, 'I have fed it, now I am exercising it so that it gives me the silver coins I was promised.' As he spoke, the bear shat. The man swooped down and triumphantly picking up a silver coin, put it in his bag. The merchant's eyes lit up. The possibilities this bear presented were exciting. He began haggling with the man who agreed only after the bid reached two thousand silver coins. The man also added, 'But I will also take away all the coins it has already dropped.' The merchant readily assented; what need did he have for the few measly coins when he owned the mint itself.

The man walked on to the city. He stopped on the outskirts and taking a beautiful *daura suruwal* from the bundle, put it on. He then hid the rest of the clothes and taking the money, went to the palace. In the court, the king was playing cowries with his courtiers. Seeing the well-dressed, prosperous-looking man, the king mistook him for a merchant and invited him to join the game. Bankrolled by the money he had swindled, the man confidently sat down. When asked what his name was, the man replied, 'Kakaji.'

Meanwhile, all the people Kakaji had conned met up, one by one, on the road. They discussed their misfortune and decided that only the king could set right the great wrongs that had been done to them. When they reached the palace, they were told to wait while the king finished his game. But they were now no longer sure of the man's identity. While Kakaji did look like the man who had swindled them, he was wearing good clothes and had the ear of the king. If they accused him and were wrong, the king's wrath would fall on them. They kept quiet. Kakaji saw and heard the people who had come to nab him but betrayed no emotion and kept playing.

Soon, the king threw down the cowries and turning to the man, said, 'Kakaji, what will your bet be?' Hearing the king address the conman as his *kaka*, uncle, the victims of the conman lost heart and went away. After all of them had left, the man played a few more hands and when he was still ahead, quit the game and took his leave.

He reached home with the bundle of clothes and money and gave them to his wife. She was overjoyed and from then on, never once complained about his laziness.

The Greatest of All

There was once a beautiful lady-rat. Every male rat in her community wanted to marry her but she was very picky and quite arrogant. She would tell all the suitors that they were unworthy. Soon, word spread that she was hard to please and the male rats stopped proposing marriage to her. She kept waiting for the perfect husband for some years but when none met her exacting standards, she began to worry. The lady-rat then retreated to the jungle to pray to Lord Vishnu. He was pleased with her penance and appearing before her, gave her a boon. The lady-rat wanted Lord Vishnu to give her the power to make anyone whom she wanted to marry, marry her. Her wish was granted.

The lady-rat then went back to her community and asked other rats who the most powerful being was. All of them said that the sun was the most powerful being; without his warmth, nothing could survive. She looked up at the sun and said, 'O sun, you are the most powerful being there is, marry me.'

The sun looked down at the tiny rat staring up at him, arms on hips, and said, 'I would be delighted, but there is one who is more powerful than I am.'

The lady-rat eagerly asked, 'Who could be more powerful than you?'

The sun replied, 'As resplendent as I am, a single cloud can waft across my face and blot me out for days. I definitely think that the clouds are more powerful than me.'

The lady-rat agreed and, determined to find the most powerful being, walked off in search of a cloud. She looked up at one and said, 'O cloud, who can the blot the face of the mighty sun, marry me.'

The cloud looked down and said, 'It would be a great honour, but there still is one who is more powerful than me.'

The lady-rat eagerly asked, 'And who is more powerful than you?'

The cloud replied, 'I can prevent the sun from spreading his warmth but I am at the mercy of even the gentlest of breezes. They push me around wherever they want.'

The lady-rat left abruptly to look for the breeze. She came upon him pushing some clouds along without even half trying. She accosted him, 'O breeze, lord of the clouds, marry me.'

The breeze swirled down and about the lady-rat, whom he could easily pick up and deposit elsewhere, and said, 'It would be a great pleasure to marry you but even I, who can push clouds about at will, have someone who is greater than I am.'

When asked who could be greater, the breeze replied, 'The mountain stands tall and immovable. Even when I put on my most fearsome aspect, rage and batter him, he stands firm. And when he stands in my way I am helpless.'

The lady-rat did an about face and without another word, walked off in search of the mountain. When she came upon him, she asked, 'O mountain, who can stop even the most powerful gales, marry me.'

The mountain peered down at the tiny rodent standing at his feet and said, 'It is true that the wind is powerless against me, and I would dearly love to accede to your request, but I must confess that there is one who is still greater than me.'

The rat sighed, would this never end? She asked, 'And who can be greater than the mighty mountain?'

The mountain replied, 'You rats. You build your tunnels and burrows in me and cause the most damage. Every year I suffer the most grievous injuries when it rains: the water enters your burrows and causes landslides. You will be the cause of my extinction one day.'

The lady-rat realized the truth of the mountain's words. Didn't she build burrows and tunnels all the time? Convinced that it was rat-kind who was the most powerful of all, she went back to her community. There she sought out the most handsome rat she could find and married him. The couple, convinced about their greatness, lived happily ever after.

The Love Story of the Uttis Tree

Thousands of years ago, when gods still took an active interest in the affairs of the world, there was the custom that trees would marry. On a hill in the north of Nepal, there was a beautiful forest. The trees grew strong and green and come spring, would put forth their flowers and light up the entire forest with their many colours.

All the trees in the forest were unmarried and this state of affairs pained the *Pipal* tree, designated, because of his great height, as the matchmaker. He decided that he would be the one to fix the first marriage in the forest; something he would always be known for. He set forth. He looked far and wide, and standing near the top of the hill, found the *Laligurans*, rhododendron, tree. The Pipal tree asked her, 'O beautiful Laligurans, whose flowers crown our canopy, you have come of age. It is only right that the first marriage in this forest should be yours. Do I have your permission to look for a husband for you?'

The Laligurans shyly replied, 'I am honoured that you would look for a husband for me. I will certainly marry any tree if he is right for me.'

The Pipal then began to look for a suitable groom. He searched through the scorching summer, the wet monsoon and when autumn passed, he had still not found anyone he thought worthy of the stunning Laligurans. And then, one day, in the dead of winter, he came upon the *Uttis* tree standing tall, proud and evergreen in the snow. He went up to him and said, 'I have been looking for someone like you all year. I have brought a marriage proposal for you from the beautiful Laligurans, whose flowers can be surpassed by no other tree in the forest. She lives just beyond yonder hill, very near the summit.'

The Uttis tree drew himself up to his full height and said loftily, 'How can I be sure unless I see her for myself?'

The Pipal readily agreed to take the Uttis to the Laligurans. They set out immediately but when they reached the summit and looked down on the Laligurans, a strange sight greeted them. Winter had stripped the Laligurans of all her lustrous foliage and had left her naked and shivering in the icy winds. The Uttis turned angrily on the Pipal, 'What is the meaning of this? You brought me all the way only to show me this wretch? Bah!' He stalked away. Perplexed at what had happened to the Laligurans, the Pipal tree sheepishly followed. All winter, he thought about what had happened and in the spring went to the Uttis, 'O noble Uttis, perhaps I made a mistake by taking you to the Laligurans in winter. Please consider visiting her now.' The uttis, at first, steadfastly refused but when the Pipal described to him, once again, all her charms, he agreed reluctantly.

They set off and soon reached the summit. What the Uttis saw floored him. The Laligurans was covered in the first flush of spring. Every leaf and every red flower was bathed in the fresh, new sunlight and the gentle breeze showed off a new aspect of her beauty with every scamper. The Uttis looked at the Pipal tree and implored him to get the Laligurans to agree to be his bride.

The Pipal went up to Laligurans and asked, 'O beautiful laligurans, strong, noble, evergreen Uttis requests your hand in marriage. Will you agree to be his wife?'

The Laligurans looked up at the Pipal tree and said, 'In winter when I was shorn of all my leaves and flowers, Uttis called me a wretch. But with spring here, and my foliage back, he wants to make me his wife. He is not only insensitive, he is also shallow. Not now and not in a hundred years will I agree to be his bride.'

The Uttis, who imagined himself to be the best of all the trees in the forest, had never been spoken about like this. He turned to the Pipal tree but found no help there. In shock he stepped back and tumbled off a cliff. He prevented himself from falling to the bottom only by clinging desperately to a rock. The Pipal peered over the edge and glumly shook his head; it was because of him that this had happened. He vowed that he would never try to make any other match ever again.

Since then the Uttis tree, ashamed to show his face after the rejection, grows only in the gullies and ravines. The Laligurans, however, beautiful and pure as ever, proudly graces our hill and mountain tops.

The Goddess of Tales Gets Angry

There was once a king who was a great connoisseur of stories. Storytellers would be invited from all over the country to narrate stories. However, the king had one besetting sin: he would frequently fall asleep in the middle of the narration. He would then have to be woken up and the story would have to be repeated to him. This behaviour was a great affront to the goddess of tales. She decided to punish the king.

She appeared to the king's minister in his dream and said to him, 'I am deeply upset by your king's behaviour. When he eats rice, I will make sure there is a needle in his food. When he ingests the needle, he will die. If he survives that, I will make sure a tree branch falls on his head when he is out riding. If he survives that too, then a snake will enter his bedroom and bite him to death. If you tell the king any of this, you will immediately be turned to stone.' The minister woke up with a start and spent the rest of the night tossing and turning in his bed in great agitation.

He reached the royal court the next morning, looking

haggard and tired. When the king asked him why he was looking tired, he only replied, 'I had a rough night, your Highness,' and did not elaborate.

The minister stuck close to his king all morning and at breakfast, requested the king to sift through his rice. The king, to humour a favoured minister, went through the mound of rice. Much to his surprise, he found a needle on his plate. He thanked the minister for his foresight which saved his life. One danger had been averted but two remained. The minister begged the king to try and remain awake through the story-telling session that was to follow breakfast. When the king asked his minister why, the minister only said, 'Your Highness, you have humoured me once today, please just do as I say.' The note of urgency in the normally unflappable minister's voice struck the king and he agreed. However, by the time the storyteller had reached the middle of his tale, the king was snoring peacefully. That night was another restless one for the minister.

The next day, when the king went out hunting, his minister rode close to him. After riding for some time, the hunting party decided to rest. The king was sitting under a tree when a large branch broke off with a loud crack and plummeted straight for him. The minister was alert to the danger and pulled the king out from the path of the falling branch in the nick of time. The king was very grateful and not a little surprised that his minister had saved him from sure death for the second time in two days. He asked the minister what the matter was; why he was looking so nervous and on edge all the time. His minister dodged a reply, only saying that he wasn't sleeping well. He then insisted, again, that the king was not to sleep during the story-telling session. The king, though intrigued, did not press for a reply and agreed. The strenuous exercise and a heavy meal, however, had done their trick. The king fell asleep in the middle of a phrase.

The goddess had threatened the king with one more danger, a snake. The minister was determined to protect his king and after the storyteller had left, sneaked into the king's bedroom. He hid in a cupboard to wait for the snake. When he could hear the king and queen peacefully snore, he opened the door of the cupboard a tiny inch so that he could have an unobstructed view of the royal bed. The goddess had kept her word. At midnight, he saw a snake slither on to the bed. The minister sprang out and with his sword, cut the snake into two. The snake, which had appeared miraculously, now vanished. The commotion woke the queen who, seeing the minister stand over her with sword upraised, screamed. The king woke with a start and called for the guards. When the minister was securely in the grip of his guards, he told the minister that for this perfidy, he would be hanged.

The minister was faced with a dilemma. If he spoke the truth, he would be turned to stone but the circumstantial evidence against him was very strong; he could not escape hanging. He decided to preserve his honour and told the king everything. When he finished he became a stone statue. The king was filled with remorse for his action. He got the stone figure of his faithful minister installed behind his throne, conducted puja to propitiate the goddess of tales, and from that moment on, did not hear stories at all or if he did, heard them from start to finish.

The Trader from Tibet

It was a custom, and a necessity, for Nima to come to Nepal from his home in Tibet every summer for trade. It was also customary that when in Nepal he would stay with his friend Lale and his family.

One year, when Nima arrived, Lale was not at home. He had gone to some other village on urgent work and was not expected for a couple of days. Nima felt that it must have been urgent work indeed if Lale had left behind his wife and six-day-old son to attend to it. Like always, he was given food and made comfortable. Later, as he sat in the courtyard enjoying a quiet *hookah,* he thought that it would not be proper for him to sleep inside the house. He would make his bed in the courtyard. But, all the goods he had brought from Tibet were inside; what if someone was to break in and he did not wake up? No, he would sleep on the door sill. Night fell and Lale's wife went inside to sleep. The trader took up his post on the door sill and stood guard for some time. However, he was very tired and soon fell asleep.

At midnight, the goddess of fate arrived at Lale's door to write his six-day-old son's fate. She found Nima blocking her way. She nudged him; Nima immediately sprang awake.

He demanded, 'Who are you and what business do you have here in the middle of the night?'

The goddess replied, 'I am the goddess of fate. I have come to write the fate of Lale's newborn son.'

Nima was now curious, 'Well, you may enter but only after you tell me his fate.'

'That cannot be, Nima, no fate can be revealed before it is written.'

'Then you may not enter.'

This impasse continued till the goddess gave in and agreed to tell him the boy's fate after she had written it. When she came out, she told Nima that the boy would marry the daughter of a trader who also happened to be a good friend of his father. Then, he would inherit his father-in-law's property and spend his days in ease and luxury.

Nima asked the goddess, 'Could you tell me the name of the friend?'

The goddess replied, 'Nima, I have told you more than you needed to know. Be content.' She then vanished.

The Trader from Tibet

Nima lay down to rest and kept pondering over the words of the goddess of fate. When she mentioned a trader friend, she could only have been referring to him. But he had no daughter and even if he did, it was hardly likely that Lale's son, who would live in Nepal, could ever marry his daughter. He was confused and dismissing what the goddess said as being impossible, fell into a disturbed sleep.

The next day, Nima woke, conducted his business and the day after took his leave. He had wanted to wait for Lale to discuss his strange experience, but there was no telling when he would come back.

In Tibet, he began a new business and stopped coming to Nepal for trade. The goddess's prediction was soon forgotten. In time, his wife gave birth to a daughter and in some years, she grew up into a beautiful young girl.

It had been many years since Lale had seen Nima and he wondered what had happened to his friend. Lale decided that he must pay Nima a visit. He would take Dikpal, his son, along so that Dikpal could have an opportunity to see a new place. That spring, after many days of travel, father and son reached Tibet. They went to Nima's house and were warmly welcomed by him and his family. Lale was happy to see that in these years, Nima had become more prosperous than he had ever been as a nomadic trader. His business was running well and he was even planning branches in other parts of Tibet. For a month, Lale and Dikpal were guests at Nima's house, accompanying the trader on business as well as pleasure trips across the whole country. But summer soon came to an end and it was time for Lale and Dikpal to leave; else winter would come upon them and the mountain passes would close. One day, about a week before they were to leave, Nima sat with Lale. He told Lale, 'You have raised your son well. He has grown up to be a fine young man. I would like to keep him with me here for a year; he could help with my expansion plans and also learn in the process.'

Lale was overjoyed and said, 'Nima, nothing would please me more.' Calling Dikpal into the room, he told him that he was to stay with Uncle Nima for a year. Lale then returned to Nepal.

Working under the tutelage of such an accomplished businessman, Dikpal learnt much. He became very good friends with Dorje, Nima's son, and grew close to Tsering, his beautiful young daughter. This proximity soon blossomed into love. Dorje observed the love that had grown between his sister and Dikpal and was very happy. He went up to his father and told him about it, adding that as soon as possible, Lale and his family should be sent for and Tsering married off to Dikpal. Nima was suddenly reminded of the goddess of fate and her prophecy. Nima recognized the potential in Dikpal and was happy that he would marry his daughter. But he also remembered the rest of the prophecy: Dikpal would inherit all of his property. Nima found the notion unbearable and the prophecy obsessed him to such an extent that he decided Dikpal must die.

Nima went to a poor, greedy cobbler and told him that if he killed the person carrying the shoes Nima was now wearing when he sent that person to his shop, he would pay him in gold. The cobbler agreed.

Nima went home and requested Dikpal to go to the cobbler's to get his shoe mended. He then took off a shoe he was wearing and handed it over to Dikpal. Dikpal was just heading out to the cobbler's when he ran into Dorje. Dorje was mortified: the would-be son-in-law of the house ferrying torn shoes; this was unthinkable. He took the shoe from Dikpal and went with it to the cobbler's.

Dikpal went back home; Nima was surprised to see him.

He asked Dikpal if the shoe had been repaired. When Dikpal said that Dorje had gone to the cobbler's with the shoe, Nima rushed out without a word. He reached the cobbler's house only to see his dead son lying on the floor. He did not say anything; he paid the cobbler and came away. Nima submitted to the fate that the goddess had written for him. He died soon after, leaving everything to Dikpal. Dikpal then brought his aged parents to Tibet and they were a happy family till the end of their days.

Invisible Death

Once there lived an old man in a village with his wife and two grown-up sons. He chose brides for his sons, hoping that his daughters-in-law would look after him and his wife but they soon left to live their own lives. The old man's wife, unable to stand the heartbreak, died soon after. For some time, the old man lived as best he could on his meagre savings but when they ran out, he was forced to go to work. He would go to the forest, cut firewood and sell it in the market. It was hard work but there was no other way.

One day, he was in the forest as usual. He lopped off the branches of a dead tree and tied it into a bundle. He then hoisted the load on to his back using a *namlo* to support the load on his head. He was bent over under the weight and was making his way slowly out of the forest. He wasn't as strong as he used to be and had to rest often. He came to a *chautari*, a resting place, and rested his load there. He took out a packet of bidis and lighted one. He then began thinking of his dead wife, his heartless sons and the difficult life he was living in his old age. It all became too much and the old man, cursing his fate, cried, 'Why doesn't Death take me away?' It so happened that Death was nearby, collecting a woman's soul. He came up to the old man and asked, 'Did you call me?'

The old man was bemused and a little shocked. He asked, 'Who are you?'

Death said, 'I am Death. Didn't you call out to me just now?'

The old man believed he was being made a fool of and his face showed it. Death said to the man, 'You doubt my word. You see the woman in that river? She's going to die now.' As soon as he said this, the woman bobbed in the water a couple of times and vanished. The old man believed she was only taking a dip and would soon surface. But she didn't and a few minutes later, her lifeless body floated up. The old man felt a tremendous surge of fear; what had been only an exclamation had suddenly come to life. Convinced that the being standing in front of him was indeed Death, the old man tried to explain to him that he was only speaking rhetorically. Death understood and told the old man that he would never come for anyone before their time. The old man had no desire to argue with Death and he only asked when Death would be coming for him. Death told him, 'Five years,' and went away.

The old man now knew he had just five years to live and the greed for life overtook him. He found a huge, old tree in the forest and hollowing it out, built a maze of rooms in it. When his five years were up, Death arrived and found him sitting at the foot of the tree. He told the old man that his time was up; the old man agreed but told Death that he would like to show him what he had done in these five years. Death agreed. The old man took him through the maze of rooms and cunningly locked Death up in the innermost room. He then came back outside locking all the doors behind him.

With Death trapped in the old man's maze, no one on earth died. The population kept increasing and food became scarce. Worse, people became old, decrepit and were unable to take care of themselves but would not die. The cycle of creation had been gravely tampered with and the balance on earth was going awry. The gods were distressed and they all went to Lord Vishnu. Vishnu, being all-seeing, knew exactly where Death was. He disguised himself as an ordinary man and came down to earth. He went to the old man who was still sitting at the foot of his tree, unimaginably old, weak and spent. His sunken eyes looked up at Vishnu and they told the story of a life that had stretched too long.

Vishnu asked the old man, 'Do you still want life?'

The man, with great effort, said no. In fact, if his wasted muscles had even an ounce of power, he would walk through the maze and free Death.

Vishnu then asked him, 'If I give you enough power to free Death, will you do so?'

For the first time, Vishnu saw animation in the old man's eyes. The god willed the old man to stand up and walk. The old man then took out a bunch of old, rusted keys from his waistband and led Vishnu through the maze. They came at last upon Death lying on the floor. The old man saw Death and with great peace on his face, lay on the floor and died. The curse of eternal imprisonment had extracted a heavy toll from Death; he was just a bundle of rags. Filth caked his body and hair, and he was weak and pale. Vishnu was so moved by the sight that he immediately restored Death to his former state of good health. Death then requested Lord Vishnu to take away from him the responsibility of collecting people's souls. But Vishnu told Death that the cycle of creation could continue only when Death did his job. However, if there was anything that could make Death's job easier, Vishnu was willing to grant it. And that is why today Death is invisible.

The King's Barber

The king's barber presumed himself to be an important man. He worked exclusively for the court and the fact that even the royal neck must submit to his keen razor thrilled and gratified him. The barber was also discontented. He imagined he worked more than all the other employees of the court and was not at all happy with the remuneration he received. He was convinced that the king's minister—who must surely be spreading canards about him—was preventing the king from raising his salary. The more the barber thought about this, the more his blood boiled. He worked himself up to such a pitch that he soon firmly believed that the minister must die for him to make any progress at all in the royal court. He began to scheme.

One morning, as he was giving the king his daily massage, the barber said, 'Your Highness, I met your father in my dream last night.' The king, who was utterly relaxed under the barber's expert fingers, sleepily asked, 'What did he say?' The barber, kneading the kinks away from the royal back, said, 'He seemed sad, Sire. He told me that he is lonely in heaven.' The king was interested; he turned around and faced the barber. The barber sensed his opportunity and said, 'He told me that he wants your minister for company.' The king thought about what the barber had said. If his father really was lonely in heaven, it was his duty as son to do something about it.

He summoned his minister. When the minister arrived, the king told him that he must make preparations to go to heaven; his company was urgently needed by his father, the former king. When he heard this absurd order, the minister immediately understood something was not right. This was a conspiracy to get rid of him. He thought quickly and said to the king, 'Your Highness, it would be an honour for me to give company to your father. But, if it would not be a great inconvenience, I pray that you grant me four days to settle my affairs.' The king was overjoyed with his minister's loyalty and readily agreed.

In the four days that were granted to him, the minister did some scheming of his own. He conducted discreet enquiries and found out that it was the barber who was responsible for the predicament he was in. He also got some of his most trusted followers to sabotage the pyre he was to ascend to heaven from. He got them to dig a tunnel underneath the place where the pyre would be set up and covered it up with a stone sliding door.

On the fifth morning, a great crowd had gathered to witness the minister's ascension to heaven. He climbed on to the pyre with great dignity, clad in full ministerial regalia. The king had ensured that his minister, who was going to do such an important job, must be bid farewell to with the full pomp of a royal send-off. Finally, the king himself put flame to the pyre. With the flames and the smoke rising higher and blocking him from view, the minister frantically burrowed his way down into the pyre. He reached the bottom, slid the door open and crawled into the tunnel, sliding the door shut behind him. He huddled in the dark tunnel, hearing the roar of the pyre and the muffled cheers of the people outside. Slowly, the noise subsided as the people walked away. The minister kept waiting till his supporters arrived in the dead of the night and knocked on the secret door. They then spirited him away and he went into hiding.

A few days later, the king received a letter. It was
from his trusted minister and it said that his journey to
heaven had been uneventful, he had found the old king
with ease and that he was ecstatic to have his minister for
company. However, in heaven, the old king's hair and
beard had grown excessively long and was bothering him.
Also, there were no good masseurs in heaven and the
old king would be very glad to have the barber there.
The king immediately sent for the barber, who was,
naturally, still celebrating the destruction of his enemy.
He told the barber the latest news from heaven and that
he was to make preparations to go there; he was needed.
The barber turned white with fear. When he tried to
stammer a reply, the king cut him off saying, 'This is
an order.'

Paralysed, the barber could do nothing to thwart the
course of events. The king had given him four days—the
same as the minister—to get his affairs in order. On the
designated day, he was given a full state farewell as he
climbed on to the pyre. The king put flame to the pile of
wood and the barber went screaming to his death.

The minister then presented himself in court and

explained to the bewildered king the plan that the barber had laid. The king was happy that his minister was so astute and commended him for the punishment he had inflicted upon his would-be murderer.

The Potter's Plight

There was once a potter who was exceptionally skilled. The pots he made were not only beautiful, they also served their function perfectly. The potter was always looking to improve the quality of his products and the variety meant that customers came from near and far to buy his products. He was devoted to his art and to Lord Shiva who was his guardian god.

Shiva was pleased with the potter. One day, as the craftsman was offering his daily prayers prior to starting work, Lord Shiva appeared before him. He told the potter that he could have anything he wanted. The potter replied that Shiva had already given him all he needed and there really wasn't anything he desired. But when Lord Shiva insisted, the potter requested the god to bless him so that all the pots he created would never break. Lord Shiva asked, 'Are you sure you want this?' The potter replied, 'Yes, Lord.' Then Shiva said, 'So be it,' and disappeared.

The potter then moulded a pot, fired it and then dropped

it from a height. It did not break. He was pleased with the result and began telling people about his pots which would last forever. People flocked to his house to verify his claim. When they were satisfied, they bought whatever they needed and went away. They spread the word and soon, every family in the village—and some surrounding villages—was using the unbreakable pots. The people stopped buying new utensils and the potter's business dwindled. The first few years, the family got by on savings accrued from the sale of the unbreakable pots but as the money ran out, matters became serious. They became destitute and the family was soon reduced to begging. However, the potter dared not grumble the boon was one he had asked of Lord Shiva himself. He never lost faith in Shiva and kept praying to him regularly.

Lord Shiva took pity on his devotee and appeared to the potter and said that he could have one more boon. The potter immediately requested Shiva to take away from him the ability to make everlasting pottery. Shiva said, 'So be it,' and vanished. With his pottery no longer unbreakable, the potter began to make his normal pots. Unbreakable pots too grow old and people need new ones; besides, the beauty of his new creations was such that people could not stop themselves from buying. Business gradually picked up and the potter got his life back.

The Liar and the Robbers

This is an old story. In a village in the west of Nepal lived a young boy, a habitual liar, with his mother. Theirs had been a rich family but they were now paupers with only a huge house to live in, an old donkey, and no money to their names. But they had kept up the facade of prosperity and people imagined they had lots of wealth stashed away.

The village, in those days, was the special target of a gang of robbers who had made a nearby forest their lair. Every house had been targeted in turn and it looked like the robbers had kept the biggest house for the last, to ransack at leisure. It had been some time since the last raid and the young liar was sure that by nightfall, the thieves would attack his house. He was afraid that when they found nothing of value, they would torture him and his mother for treasure which did not exist. He thought up a plan. He took the final few rupees he had and went to the village market. There he exchanged the notes for coins and came back home. That night, before he went to bed, he went to the donkey shed and spread some coins in the donkey dung. He also pushed some coins up the donkey's rectum.

Sure enough, the robbers roused him from a deep slumber in the middle of the night. They had already searched the house from top to bottom and found nothing. The robbers were very angry and told the liar that if he did not tell them where all their wealth was stashed, their lives were forfeit. The boy told the robbers the truth, a rare occurrence for him: he and his mother had nothing except the crumbling house and an old donkey. The robbers, to have at least something to show for the night's labours, decided to take the donkey. At this, the liar cried, if anything, the robbers could take him and make him their slave but his old mother could not survive without the donkey. Now their interest was tickled: what was so special about a mangy old donkey that his mother could not live without it? They asked the boy to lead them to the animal. In the shed they lit a *tuki*, a lamp. The donkey seemed ordinary. The robbers, threatening physical violence, asked the boy to tell them what was special about the animal and the boy feigning great reluctance, told the robbers that the donkey shat coins. When they heard this, the robbers poked about in the dung and found some of the coins the boy had secreted. The robbers then asked the boy to prove to them that the donkey shat coins. The boy started beating the animal, and out of fear, it dropped some dung. The droppings were flecked with coins of various denominations. The robbers had hit jackpot. As they led the donkey away, the liar let out yet another howl of protest which earned him a slap. The robbers told him that he should consider it a matter of great fortune that his life was being spared. After all, they were leaving behind the coins that the donkey had already dropped. A crisis had been averted but the liar was sure that when the robbers found they had been duped, they would come for him. He set out to make preparations. That very night he went to the forest. The next morning the liar came back with two wolf cubs he had trapped. He gave one to his mother and told her to hide it somewhere. He then instructed her that if the robbers came, she should send them to him in the forest and then prepare some food.

The robbers came to the liar's house the next day and asked his mother about him. She said that he was in the forest. The robbers found him lazing under a tree and playing with the cub. The robbers were angry with the liar. Not only did the donkey not shit any more coins, when they had beaten it, it had died. The liar began to weep. The donkey had supported his family, but now it was dead. The animal was old and the robbers should have only pretended to beat it; it took some time and familiarity with new owners for the donkey to give coins. When the robbers told the liar to shut up and threatened to kill him, he told them that nothing could come of his murder. If the robbers let him live, he would give them the coins that they had left behind for him the and all food that was cooked in his house. He then turned to the cub and told the little creature to run home and tell the liar's mother to prepare a feast for the robbers. When the liar untied the cub, it promptly scampered off into the forest. The robbers were wonder-struck; first a donkey which shat coins and now this: a wolf cub that understood human speech. Curious, they followed the liar home.

They reached the liar's house to find a feast laid out for them in the courtyard. They wanted to know if it was indeed the cub which had brought the news home. The liar told his mother to bring the cub around, explaining casually to the robbers that it had the unfortunate habit of interrupting their meals. The robbers had found something to show for their labours. But when they asked for the cub, the liar told them that after they had mistreated and killed his donkey, he was loath to give them the cub, even if it meant death. He would much rather let it go free. But the robbers; instead of threatening someone who obviously knew magic, tried to bargain with him. They would let him keep the money the donkey had produced; they would also pay him more money. With much feigned reluctance, the liar agreed. After the deal was struck, they ate; the robbers paid the liar and walked away with the cub.

The robbers had run out of houses to rob so they decided to rob another village. Half the gang stayed behind. The other half took the cub along intending to send it back with a message if they wanted food ready on their return. They reached the outskirts of the village by dusk and waited. The whole village was singing *bhajans*, sitting under a pipal tree. There was no question of robbing any house. They decided to wait and carefully told the cub to go back to the hideout and tell the others to prepare food for them. The cub ran off into the undergrowth. The robbers at the hideout decided that the others would not need food so they ate and went to sleep.

Late at night, the robbers came back from an unsuccessful expedition: the singing didn't stop and they were feeling hungry. The hideout was dark and everyone was sleeping. They woke everyone up and demanded to know where the food was. Those who stayed back said that the cub had never come home. And, they wanted to know why they were empty-handed. Was it because they had hidden the loot elsewhere? A serious argument began to brew and was about to become a scuffle when one of the robbers pointed out that the wolf cub was nowhere to be seen. The discussion took on a new direction; perhaps they had been made fools of. Full of wrath brought on by interrupted sleep, hunger and a wasted day, they went to the liar's house.

When they knocked on the door, they found it unlocked. They went inside and saw the liar pacing furiously from room to room muttering, 'Now, where did I keep that herb?' His mother was lying on a cot, apparently dead. When he saw the robbers, he began to cry, 'I am an orphan. My mother is dead.' The robbers were caught off guard and said nothing. The boy continued to rummage through the house and soon came out of a room, triumphantly holding up some dried herbs. Without saying anything to the robbers, he went to the kitchen and came out holding a glass of murky water. He wet the lips of his dead mother and opening her mouth, put a few drops of the water on her tongue. Miraculously, the old lady came to life. The robbers forgot all about the lost cub and asked the boy what he had given his mother. He told them that these were herbs which not only brought the dead back from life but also granted immortality. The robbers obviously wanted it. They threatened and bargained till the boy finally decided to give them some in return for money.

The robbers walked away, happy that they could now steal for all of eternity. They divided the herbs into equal parts, everyone took it and promptly fell dead; the herbs were poison. Rid of the thieves, the liar, his mother and the entire village lived happily till the end of their days.

The Liar and the Robbers

The Owl and the Elephant

An owl and an elephant were great friends. They lived very close to each other in the jungle and would meet every morning and evening: in the morning the owl would be coming back from his nocturnal hunting expeditions while the elephant would be going out to feed; in the evening the order of going and coming was reversed. When they met, they would discuss normal, everyday things like the weather and where each was going, or how good their trips had been. The bond between the two was very strong.

One morning in summer, the elephant told the owl that he would have to venture further into the forest to look for green leaves; the sun was drying out all the greenery. He set out and his enormous appetite took him deeper and deeper into the heart of the jungle. Absorbed in finding the best, greenest buds, he failed to realize that demons had made their home in the middle of the jungle. He suddenly looked up and saw a group of them sitting in the middle of a clearing. He was frightened and decided to carefully slink away. As he stepped slowly back, his foot came down on a dry stick and it broke with a resounding crack. He winced, this was a mistake he would have never made if he hadn't been nervous. The demons, blessed with supernatural hearing, naturally heard the sound. They saw the elephant and licked their chops with glee. This was the most amazing luck; the prey had walked right into their lair. They quickly secured the elephant. But, as was custom, any prey had to be presented to their chief before they could feast. They dragged the helpless elephant into the royal presence. The king was overjoyed. He roared his approval and told all his sycophants that only the other night he had dreamt that he was eating an elephant. The elephant felt faint but, summoning all his courage, told the king that he was honoured that his humble, lowly body would feed such an exalted, royal personage. He said many such sugary, flattering words and when the king of demons had swollen up with pride, put forward his story. A solitary elephant, abandoned by his herd, he had only one friend in the whole world, an owl. He would like to meet him once before he died. Filled with a sense of his own importance and benevolence, the king agreed. Thus, accompanied by two demons, the elephant set off.

When he reached the owl's perch, he asked the demon guards to stop at a distance. He woke the sleeping owl and quickly told him of his plight. The owl thought quickly and then put on a great, elaborate show of grief. He convinced the demons that he must be at his friend's side when the last moment arrived. The demons reluctantly agreed and they went back, with the owl perched on the elephant's back.

As soon as the group reached the king, the owl demanded loudly, 'Now, where is the princess? She came to me in a dream last night; I am supposed to be marrying her.'

The king replied, 'What nonsense is this! How can you demand to marry someone just because you dreamt of the marriage?'

The owl replied, 'But, Your Highness, you yourself are going to eat my friend because you were eating elephant flesh in your dream; why should I, then, be not allowed to marry your daughter whom I married in my dream?'

The king had no answer to the owl's question and agreed to let the two of them go free.

Gonu Jha and the Robbers

G onu Jha and his wife lived in the eastern terai of Nepal. They were a lovely couple, and a subject of great curiosity to all their neighbours, for Gonu Jha—apart from minor sharecropping for a local *zamindar*, landlord— did no work yet the couple managed to live reasonably well. But the answer, really, was quite simple. Gonu Jha possessed great wit and he could make others do all his work for him.

It had been some time since Gonu had pulled off a caper and his wife began to wonder how long they could keep running the house on the profits from his last project. Gonu went to the zamindar and asked him for some land to sharecrop for some time. The zamindar was surprised. He had never known Gonu to take any initiative at all as far as agriculture was concerned. He asked Gonu why he needed the land. When Gonu told the landlord that he needed the land for cultivation, the zamindar was shocked. He was certain that it was beyond Gonu to do any honest labour so he purposely told Gonu to farm a certain piece of land which everyone, including Gonu, knew was barren. Gonu happily agreed and walked off.

That evening, Gonu asked his wife to tie farm implements—rake, shovel, hoe, etc—into a bundle and keep it ready. After dinner, he walked out into the darkness in the direction of the barren land. His wife sat on the doorstep and watched him walk away, wondering what her uncommonly resourceful husband was now up to.

When he reached the plot of land, Gonu worked hard for an hour, digging furiously. He then lay underneath a tree and rested. At midnight, a group of men he knew to be robbers passed the field on one of their nocturnal missions. He quickly jumped up and made a great show of digging the land. The robbers saw him and were, naturally, curious. Gonu Jha told them that Lakshmi, the goddess of riches, had said to him in a dream that great riches were hidden in the land; if they helped him find it, he would share the wealth with them. The robbers were happy and fell to the work with gusto. But they dug till dawn broke and found nothing. The robbers were weary and greatly angry, and they knew they had been roundly cheated: it was obvious that they had been made to dig up fallow land.

They looked for Gonu Jha but he was, obviously, not to be found. They left vowing that when the crop was ready, they would come and take it all away.

Gonu Jha, pleased that the first part of his plan had been successfully completed, swaggered to the zamindar's house and told him that he would need seeds to plant. The zamindar could not believe that Gonu had gotten the land ready overnight and refused to hand the seeds over till he saw the prepared land for himself. Gonu took him to the land the robbers had dug, and the zamindar, forced to believe the evidence of his own eyes, gave Gonu the seeds. The next day, Gonu and his wife planted the crop.

It was soon harvest time. Gonu began to keep vigil. And, true to their word, the robbers came one night and harvested the entire crop. After they had tied the crop into bundles, Gonu began to shout loudly, 'Stop, thieves! Villagers, these people are taking my crop away.' The robbers, fearing capture, ran away leaving everything behind.

The next morning, Gonu leisurely walked to the zamindar's and asked to borrow a bullock cart. The landlord, disbelievingly, gave Gonu the cart and Gonu came back with the landlord's shore.

Gonu knew that the robbers had been fooled twice and would surely be looking for revenge. He readied himself for a break-in. One night the robbers broke into his house and began looking for the stored grain. Gonu was hiding in the granary and as each robber poked his head inside, cut off his nose. The robbers were in great agony but could not say anything; to have one's nose cut off is the most shameful thing to happen to any man. They all just ran about, trying to stop the bleeding.

Ever resourceful, Gonu had prepared poison for the robbers. He shouted, 'Wife, I have cut myself, where's the medicine that stops wounds from bleeding?'

His wife replied, equally loudly, 'It's in the attic, just under the roof.' The robbers rushed to the attic, applied poison to the bleeding stumps, and died. Gonu then wrapped up the bodies in identical bags.

He couldn't have kept the bodies in his house forever. The next morning, he set out in search of a *pode*, someone who traditionally dealt with the disposal of dead bodies. He found just such a man and Gonu told him that he had a body that needed to be disposed. The two agreed on an amount to be paid on completion of the task. That evening the pode came to Gonu's house and took away the body. He threw the corpse off a cliff and came back to collect his payment. But Gonu showed him another body and said that the body he had taken away had come back and needed to be taken away again. The man took the body and threw it again. This went on till the pode had thrown away all the bodies. When he was taking away the last body, he saw a man walking out of the river into which he had been throwing the bodies off the cliff. The pode that something strange was happening; Gonu was obviously some kind of a magician. Fearing that he would have to thus ferry the dead forever, the pode ran away without taking payment. Gonu had enough food to last him the year and, in the process, had rid his village of some notorious robbers.

Yagyarath

A farmer used to sow paddy in his fields. But every season, just as the crop ripened, a flock of parrots would descend and lay the crop to waste. After this happened for a couple of seasons, the farmer decided that he needed to do something about these errant birds. He prepared a trap and when the birds swooped down on the rice, caught them all.

He then took the parrots out one by one and started killing them. But one parrot, afraid that they would all be killed in this manner, spoke up, 'O farmer, please don't kill us.' The farmer replied, 'You destroy my crop and if I let you go, you will come back next season. The least I can do with you is to prepare a tasty stew.'

The parrot replied, 'But brother, we are small and not even a mouthful. Trust me, I will be of more use to you alive than dead.'

'You, of what possible use can you be?'

'I will tell you if you promise to let my friends go free.'

The farmer was now curious. Perhaps, this parrot had magical powers.

When he had set the other parrots free, with the strong admonition that they were never to return to his fields again, the parrot told him, 'You must take me to the market and sell me.'

'Sell you! You can't be worth much.'

'Just do as I say. I will fix my own price.'

When they reached the market, the farmer put the parrot on a high perch. It began crying out its own virtues in a display of excellent salesmanship. A shopkeeper noticed and asked the farmer how much he wanted for the salesman-parrot. The parrot quickly replied, 'One thousand silver-coins.' One thousand silver coins was a lot of money and the shopkeeper hesitated. But the parrot forcefully made its case and the shopkeeper handed over the money to the farmer who gleefully walked off.

The shopkeeper set up the parrot's perch near the shop's entrance and the bird would call out loudly to advertise the products. The novelty of a parrot calling out bargains and sales proved irresistible. People came from far and wide to see the bird and sales soared. The shopkeeper became a rich man in a matter of few months.

The shopkeeper and his wife were childless and this

was the one thing in his life that bothered him a great deal. The parrot was aware of this lack in its owner's life. One day, he suggested to the shopkeeper that it would tell him a remedy if he promised to set it free.

When the shopkeeper agreed, the parrot told him of a *yagya*, a ritual, to be performed on a certain day of the year after which his wife was sure to conceive. The shopkeeper was very happy and conducted the yagya on the date he was told about. Sure enough, a few months later, his wife conceived. In due time, she gave birth to a baby boy whom they named Yagyarath.

Yagyarath grew up but the shopkeeper, despite repeated reminders, either ignored or postponed the parrot's requests to be set free. The parrot finally demanded a firm answer and to keep his word, the shopkeeper agreed. But, he was shrewd. He knew the parrot to be intelligent so he asked it to take Yagyarath along and teach him about life and all the skills that were necessary to be successful. Since it was unlikely that it would be released if it refused, the parrot agreed.

The parrot took Yagyarath along and taught him everything it knew. Once it was sure that there was nothing more it could teach Yagyarath, the parrot asked the boy to go home.

As Yagyarath made his way home, he ran into a gang of robbers. When the thieves asked him who he was, Yagyarath told them he was a thief, hoping that they would not harm one of their kind. But the thieves were shrewd; they asked him to prove his identity by stealing the eggs from a crow's nest—an impossible task. But the parrot had taught him well; he climbed up the tree, brought down the eggs and the crows did not find out anything. So impressed were the thieves by this feat of extraordinary cunning that they made him the leader of their group.

The thieves had been on their way to rob the palace and now it was up to Yagyarath to lead them. The palace wall was tall and its ramparts well-guarded. The only place they could hope to gain access was through the back wall. They waited till the clock struck twelve. While each gong resounded across the city, and masked all other sounds, the robbers heaved mighty blows at the wall. When the last gong struck, the robbers broke through.

They entered the palace and loaded their bags with the most precious things they could lay their hands on. But just as they were about to leave, one of the thieves misjudged the weight of a big brass candleholder and dropped it. The sound woke the king and he raised an alarm. The thieves ran with whatever they had. All of them managed to escape through the hole except one, who got stuck in the opening. One of the guards managed to grab him by the legs and would not let go. Yagyarath saw that his comrade would be captured and would reveal the identities of the others. To forestall this, he quickly drew his *khukri* and chopped off the head of the thief who was stuck. The sudden release of the tension meant that the guard, who was pulling the thief by the legs, fell down while the rest of the thieves made off with the head.

The king called an urgent meeting of his ministers to discuss this breach of security. If they had captured this thief alive, he may have led the guards to the others but without the head even identification was impossible. One wise minister stood up and suggested that if the cremation of the dead thief were to be publicly announced, his friends might, presumably, bring the head to be cremated with the body. The king agreed that this was indeed a workable plan and ordered its execution. The cremation was widely announced and the area in which the body was to be burnt was sealed off. The body was then cremated publicly and with great ceremony. At the end, when most of the people who had gathered to see the spectacle had walked away, an *aghori sadhu* approached the guards. He told them that the rules of the monastic order he belonged to permitted him to eat only that food which had been cooked on a funeral pyre. He had a pot of maize which he would like to roast; would the guards permit him? At first the guards were a little shocked and shooed him away but when he pleaded with them, saying that he was faint with hunger, they agreed: after all, they would be gaining some merit by feeding a holyman. The aghori put his pot on the pyre and began chatting with the guards who were very interested in this man who would eat food only if it was prepared on a pyre. Time soon passed and one of the guards pointed out that the sadhu's pot had been in the fire for a very long time. The aghori turned his attention to the pot and began crying that the only food he had, had been burnt to cinders. He blamed the guards for distracting him and began making a scene. Fearful of the attention the aghori was attracting, the guards gave him some coins and shooed him away.

Later, when the king asked if anyone had approached the funeral pyre, the guards lied, fearing retribution. The king then turned to his minister and asked why his plan had fallen through. The minister had no answer so he did not say anything. A little later, a bearer arrived with a letter on a tray. The king read the letter and turning to his guards asked why they had lied. The guards said that they feared the royal wrath. At this, the king told them that they were, indeed, justified in having such a fear. He ordered them to be taken prisoners. The minister realized that they were up against some very smart robbers. He would have to personally take charge of the matter. He asked the king for leave from the court, so that he could go out and look for the thieves. The king readily agreed.

Setting his extensive network of spies to work, the minister found that a group of robbers had taken up residence in the nearby forest. He decided to go into the forest, with some military back-up, to try and catch the thieves. On his way, the group ran into Yagyarath, disguised as a *yogi*, sitting near the road. He had a lighted *chillum* in his hand and the sickly sweet smell of cannabis pervaded the air. A bull sat behind the yogi idly chewing the cud.

To the minister, the yogi, with his matted hair bunched on top of his head, his body smeared with ash, and the bull sitting like Lord Shiva's mount, Nandi, looked fascinating. He stopped to pay his respects while his entourage walked on and rested some distance away. The minister began speaking to the yogi and found that he was, indeed, a learned and wise man. As they discussed the intricacies of religious philosophy, the yogi pretended to draw deeply on the chillum and passed it to the minister. The minister did not want to offend the yogi and knowing the enlightening effects of cannabis, took the chillum from him and drew the smoke into his lungs. Yagyarath had mixed a sedative with the ganja and the minister slowly drifted off. He then quickly bundled the minister into a sack and on to the bull which he then sent towards the palace.

The king impatiently waited for his minister all day but when he didn't turn up, went off into a fretful sleep. The next morning, the king looked out of his window and saw a large bull wandering with a bundle on its back. The king ordered the guards to investigate. When they opened the sack, the minister tumbled out. They splashed water on his face and he soon woke up, looking pale, bewildered and humiliated.

The king now began to feel that he himself must join the chase. To prevent himself from being recognized, he walked out of the palace in disguise. He roamed the whole forest from morning to evening but found nothing. As he was coming back to the palace, he came across Yagyarath disguised as a diseased and crippled man. Desperate for any information at all, the king asked the man if he had seen anyone go past recently. The man replied that just a few minutes ago, a man had run towards the north. The king rushed off in that direction. In the meantime, Yagyarath swaddled a coconut in cloth and threw it into a nearby pond. The king came back and asked Yagyarath again. This time Yagyarath told the king that the man had again come rushing back, and for some reason, had waded into the pond to hide. If the king just stretched a little, he could see the man's head bobbing on the surface. The king could see that there was, indeed, someone in the pond. He took off his clothes and waded into the pond. But as he approached the 'head', it only drifted off further. And, finally, when he did manage to nab his man, he found only a coconut. Incensed, he turned

Yagyarath

towards the shore only to find that the cripple had disappeared with his clothes and horse.

Yagyarath rode to the palace. In the dim light the guards recognized the king's disguise and let him in. He told them that very soon, a naked, crazy man would come to the door and demand entry, claiming to be king. Under no circumstances was this man to be let in. If he persisted, he was to be clapped in irons and thrown into prison. Yagyarath went into the palace but left immediately by the back door.

The king arrived later, naked and shivering with cold. He shouted to be let in. The guards ignored him. But when he demanded that they open the door for their king, the guards caught him and put him into jail. But morning brought new light and the guards recognized their mistake. Humbly begging for forgiveness, they let him out.

The king realized that this was no ordinary thief; he was impressed by Yagyarath's intelligence and presence of mind. He gathered his ministers and all agreed that a foe who could not be vanquished needed to be befriended. He had it proclaimed that not only was he willing to drop the charges against Yagyarath, he would also receive the princess' hand in marriage and half of his country.

Yagyarath heard about the king's declaration and came to the palace the next day and told everything about himself. The king then requested the royal pundit to find an auspicious date for the marriage and gave Yagyarath half the state. Yagyarath got his parents to live with him in his palace and he lived happily with his parents and wife.

The Wily Fox

There was a village near a forest and in the forest lived a very clever fox. The village was famous for its chickens and every family kept a flock. The birds were easy pickings for the fox and he was slowly fattening. He used to be very careful about eating the chickens and only occasionally lifted one but as his confidence grew, so did his greed and appetite. The occasional missing chicken missed the keen eyes of the villagers but when almost every family reported daily disappearances, the villagers got together to try and find out what was picking off their birds one by one. The fox, full of wiles, stood behind the group and shouted, 'It is the kite!'

Everyone looked up to spot the kite that was responsible for the carnage and in the confusion, the fox made off with yet another bird. This continued for some days till the villagers began to suspect that something was not right; they never did see the kite. They decided that when they were all looking up, one should try and see who was tricking them. The fox, as usual, made his move but an alert spotter pounced on him. They trussed him up securely and began to discuss what should be done to the fox. One man suggested that he should be hanged by the neck. Someone else said that he should be shot. But everyone soon agreed that these punishments would not be painful; this chicken-robber should die an agonizing death. The people decided that he should be dragged on gravel till the skin flayed off his flesh. But when they did drag the fox over grit and gravel, he appeared to be immensely enjoying it; almost as if a terrible itch was being soothed. Seeing this, the villagers dragged him over grassy ground. Here, the fox made all manner of protests and howled in mortal pain and fear. The villagers dragged him over the grassy ground till they tired. Then they hung the fox by his paws at a crossroads with a sign that said: 'This fox is a thief. Kick him.' Everyone who passed the crossroads paused to aim a kick at the hanging fox.

Eventually, a bear trundled along. When he saw the bear in the distance, the fox built some momentum and began swinging like a pendulum, smiling through the pain. The bear asked him what he was doing. The fox replied, 'I am swinging.' The bear told the fox that what he was doing seemed enjoyable, could he do it? The fox said. 'Go away, I don't want to share my swing with anybody.' But the bear was hooked, he insisted until the fox finally gave in. He tied the bear to the tree, changed the sign to read: 'This bear is a thief. Kick him', and walked away.

The beating had made him hungry and he began scavenging for food. He came upon a buffalo carcass that had been washed ashore by the river. He circled the enormous dead animal and looked for a way to get at all the flesh. He gnawed at the thigh but the animal was old and its hide was too tough for his jaws. He then burrowed into the animal through the rectum; the soaking in the water had softened that part of the animal. He then happily gnawed away at the entrails, eating his fill. He lost track of time and the sun blazing outside tightened the skin of the carcass and shut tight the fox's exit. He tried to claw his way out but could not. It so happened that the gods Mahadev and Parvati, in human form, were passing the carcass at that very instant. They heard the scratching and Mahadev asked, 'Who is it?"

The fox shouted his reply, 'Who are you?'

Mahadev said, 'I am Mahadev, the god of the gods.'

'What proof do I have that you are who you say you are?'

Mahadev was a little surprised; whatever was speaking from inside the carcass of the buffalo was in no position to be asking questions. Yet he decided to go along. He asked, 'What do you want me to do to prove my identity?'

The fox said, 'Make it rain.'

Mahadev willed the rain to fall and it did. The water soaked the carcass and when the passage the fox had created relaxed enough, he slid out and slunk away into the forest. Mahadev realized that he had been used and had been made a fool of in front of his consort. He decided to teach the fox a lesson.

He created a life-like dummy of a young boy and put glue all over it. He then put some delicious sweetmeats on the dummy's hands and stood it at a spot in the forest where he knew the fox would come. When the fox saw the dummy, he thought he was in luck; the boy was young and the fox could easily the wrest the sweets away from him. He first warned the boy to hand over the sweets but the boy made no reply. Incensed, the fox hit the boy but his hand stuck to the dummy because of the glue. Then he tried freeing himself with his other hand and feet, but only managed to hopelessly enmesh himself in the glue. Mahadev wanted to punish the fox but Parvati was very taken by this creature who had managed to pull the wool over her husband's all-seeing eyes. She implored with Mahadev to spare the fox and Mahadev, on the condition that he would never do any mischief again, set the fox free.

The Clever Wife

A merchant and his wife lived and worked in Kathmandu. They had a son who was very lazy. The merchant hoped that his son would help him out in the shop but it was impossible to make him do anything. Fed up, the couple decided that the best thing to do was to find an intelligent wife for their son who would take care of him.

The merchant went looking for a bride for his son and after many days, found a girl who fitted the bill. He met her father and asked for her hand for his son. The father refused, aware that the boy in question was good for nothing. However, the merchant kept insisting. Very soon, the girl's father began to think that though the boy was lazy and someone who might never amount to anything, his father was rich. And if his daughter married into the family, she would never want for anything. It was also true that the boy would never need to work in his life. He accepted the proposal.

In due time, the girl and the boy married. Things were smooth for the first few months but soon, a violent streak became apparent in the boy. He would beat his wife for the slightest of reasons. One day, as he was taking his shoes off to throw at his wife, she decided she had had enough. It was one thing to be married to someone who could not be bothered to do anything but to receive frequent beatings was unacceptable. She told him in no uncertain terms that a good-for-nothing like him did not have any rights at all, least of all, the right to beat his wife. She then threw a hundred rupees at him and said that if he had any self respect, he would take the money, go away, and not come back till he had made some profit.

The boy, humiliated and angry, stomped off. In his rage, he walked for hours and did not realize that it had become dark. He knocked on the door of the first house he came to. A man with only one leg opened it. He took one look at the boy and said, 'You must be the son of the man who took my false leg for repair. Have you brought it back?' The boy obviously did not understand what the one-legged man was talking about and just stood there, a bewildered expression on his face. The one-legged man began to insist and refused to let go of the boy till he returned his false leg. The boy, now afraid, was desperate to get away. He gave the one-legged man fifty rupees, half of what he had, and said that he should keep it till he returned with the false leg. Happy to get away with his skin intact, the boy dashed off.

He walked for some time before coming to another house. He knocked on the door; a one-eyed man opened it and said, 'You must be the son of the man who promised to replace my fake eye with a better one. Have you brought the replacement?' The boy, fresh from his encounter with the one-legged man, had had no time to compose himself. When matters became serious and the one-eyed man threatened violence, he fished out the fifty rupees he had left and handed the money over. He told the one-eyed man to be patient for just a little while longer and give him time to go home and bring the fake eye back. Pleased that he had saved his skin once again, he walked on. It was late and he needed shelter but this time it was important to be cautious. When he came to the next house, he looked in through the window and saw a woman preparing dinner. He made sure she had no visible physical deformities and then knocked on the door.

The woman invited him inside and made him comfortable. She served him dinner and over it mentioned a hen she owned which crowed like a rooster. The boy was feeling warm and contented and having never ventured far from home, hadn't seen enough of the world to detect any evil intention behind what the woman was saying. He was very sure of himself and refused to believe that a hen could crow. The two got into an argument and the woman craftily made the boy agree to a bet. If he won, the woman would hand over all of her property, but if he lost, he would forever forfeit his freedom and become a bonded labourer in the woman's house. The next morning, the woman woke him up early. As soon as his eyes opened, he heard a fowl crow. Lying on the bed, he couldn't be sure whether it was a hen or rooster so he hurried out into the courtyard. There, he saw a straw nest covered by a wicker basket. The woman was keenly observing matters. He lifted up the basket; inside, lying comfortably, was a hen. The woman said, quickly putting the basket back in place, 'You do believe me now when I say that my hen crows, don't you?' The boy, too stunned to believe this reversal, and, by nature, not very skilled at applying himself, dumbly agreed. He became a slave at the woman's house who promptly put him to work in the fields. Life became very tough for the boy.

Many days passed and the boy's wife began to get worried; she knew her husband's nature and was afraid that some harm had befallen him. She decided to go out to look for him. She began walking and along the way asked people if they had seen her husband. After numerous disappointments, and some success, she came to the house where the one-legged man lived. He said to her, 'You must be the wife of the boy whose father had taken my false leg for repair. The boy must have sent it with you. Do you have it?' The woman realized something was not right. She replied, 'Yes, I was sent by my father-in-law. He says that there are too many false legs for repair with him right now and he cannot recognize yours. He has asked for your other leg so that he can use it to compare.' She then took out a *khukri* and raised it to chop off the one-legged man's good leg. The one-legged man knew he was caught. He told the woman to take fifty rupees and spare him.

The girl walked on and came to the house where the one-eyed man lived. When he opened the door, he said, 'You must be the wife of the boy whose father had taken my fake eye for repair. The boy must have sent it with you. Do you have it?' The girl told him a story similar to the one she had told the one-legged man and said that she would need his good eye to check for size and fit. The one-eyed man paid the girl fifty rupees to prevent his one good eye from being gouged out. She walked on.

Finally, she reached the house where her husband was a slave. The woman, like she'd done with the girl's husband, made the girl feel welcome. She fed the girl and told her the story of the hen that crowed. The girl was perceptive and realized that things weren't what they seemed. She played along and when the woman put up the wager, agreed to it. After dinner, she went out to the courtyard to wash up. Seeing the wicker basket covering the straw nest, she lifted it and saw the hen peacefully dozing underneath. She lifted the hen and some of the straw, and found a rooster hidden in a compartment underneath the nest. She switched the hen for the rooster and carefully replacing the wicker basket, went inside and slept.

When the girl woke up the next morning, she could hear the rooster crow. The woman came in to tell her that it was the hen she was hearing. She invited the girl to go outside and check for herself. The girl boldly walked up to the nest and flipped the basket over. The rooster, startled, hopped off and ran away squawking. The girl then revealed the secret compartment and the hen in it. The woman's trickery was uncovered and the girl threatened to expose her evil designs to the authorities. The woman begged forgiveness and agreed to not only release all her slaves but also to pay the boy wages for the time he had worked for her. The girl then reunited with her husband and came back home. The boy was extremely glad to be released and was full of admiration for his intelligent wife. He then never shouted at her or beat her up, and they lived happily as man and wife.

The Clever Wife

The Fox, the Brahmin and the Tiger

There was once a Brahmin; a learned, wise and kind man. His extensive knowledge of the scriptures meant that he was frequently invited to many faraway villages to conduct religious rites. One day, he was invited to perform a *nwaran*, the naming ceremony of a newborn. To reach that particular village, the Brahmin had to cross a large forest.

The Brahmin set off early in the morning. He walked at a brisk pace wrapped in his thoughts. Suddenly, out of nowhere, he heard someone calling out to him. When he investigated, the Brahmin found that a tiger had been caught in a trap and was asking to be released. The Brahmin was about to release the tiger when he had a second thought. He said to the animal, 'I will set you free, but what guarantee do I have that you will not kill me as soon as you come out of the trap?'

The tiger appeared greatly pained by this lack of trust; he said to the Brahmin, 'But, brother, why would I even dream of killing the man who sets me free?'

The Brahmin, satisfied with the apparent genuineness of the tiger, set it free. The tiger bounded out of the trap and soon began circling the man, licking his chops. The long, forced incarceration had left him hungry and dinner had set him free. He told the man, 'Brother, I thank you for setting me free, but I am hungry and must eat.'

The Brahmin was shocked at the betrayal and the fear of imminent death made him momentarily lose his wits. But he soon pulled himself together and began to argue with the tiger, giving him many reasons why he did not deserve to be eaten. But the tiger refused to listen. Finally, the Brahmin told the tiger, 'All right, you are more powerful than I am. You can easily break my neck with one swipe of your paw. But please, as a final favour to the man who set you free, will you please walk with me along this road and ask the first three beings their opinion on if I deserve to be eaten?' The tiger, after this appeal to his magnanimity, agreed.

The two began walking and soon came to a *chautari,* a resting place for travellers. A Pipal tree stood there, spread wide and vast. The Brahmin narrated to the tree the entire incident and asked the all-important question, 'Pipal, do you think I deserve to be a meal for this tiger whom I saved from almost certain death?'

The Pipal considered briefly and said, 'Well, it is true that a tree, from the time it is a mere sapling, helps men. It gives cattle fodder and when it grows up, gives men shade, fruit, and, occasionally, dead branches for men to burn and cook their food on. And how do men repay us trees? By cutting us down for the flimsiest of reasons. Men really are the most ungrateful of all creatures on earth. You, Brahmin, deserve to die.'

The tiger stood there, silently gloating. The Brahmin, disappointed, told the tiger, 'We must walk on. We still have two more beings to meet.'

After walking for some time, the two came across a donkey. The Brahmin again narrated to the donkey the whole incident from start to finish. He then put to him the question, 'Donkey, do you think it is right that I should die thus?'

The donkey told the Brahmin, 'We donkeys are bred by you men to lift your heavy loads. All our lives you make us carry impossible burdens and when we become old and infirm, you turn us out into the streets to fend for ourselves.

And, whenever you have to refer to the stupid and the slow of mind amongst your own kind, you call them donkeys. Man is really the most treacherous of all beings. Brahmin, you deserve to die.' The tiger was now slavering at the mouth. But the Brahmin, crestfallen, reminded the tiger, 'I still have one more chance.'

A little further on, they came upon a fox which, on seeing the tiger, was slinking furtively away. But the Brahmin accosted it, 'Brother, there is a problem we want you to preside on.' He then proceeded to lay out the entire matter in front of the fox. After he had heard the full story, the fox said to the two, 'But how am I to believe that the tiger was in the trap at all?' This was a new response and the tiger was incensed. He roared, 'How dare you doubt me, you puny fox?' But the fox refused to be cowed down. He held fast to his disbelief and the impasse meant that he would have to be taken to the trap.

The fox stood before the trap inspecting it very carefully. He then said, 'Okay, I am convinced that the trap exists but I refuse to believe that this puny trap could hold such a mighty tiger at all.' The tiger was needled by this doubting fox. He told the Brahmin, 'We must show this fox we are not lying.' The Brahmin readily agreed and locked the tiger into his trap.

The fox then turned to the Brahmin and said, 'Brother, you are very kind, and you may be a wise human being, but of the principles of life, you know nothing.' Leaving behind a humbled Brahmin and a trapped, raging tiger, the fox walked away.

The Simpleton

There once lived, in a village in Nepal, a wealthy widow and her simpleton son. Her husband had been a rich landowner and had left her extensive property, but her son was such a useless fool that it was futile to expect from him any help in administering the lands. The widow began to worry that if her son did not learn some sense, there would be no one to look after all their property after her.

One day, she called him into her room and asked, 'Son, do you understand who a gentleman is?' He replied in the affirmative. She continued, 'Today, you must go out and find a gentleman. And when you find him you must tell him to take you under his wing. You must ask him to teach you everything he knows.'

The boy left. His mother had told him to head for the city; it was certain that he would find gentlemen there. On his way to the city, the simpleton had to cross a dense forest. In the middle of the forest, he came across a group of thieves. He went up to the thieves and asked them if they were gentlemen. All the robbers began laughing loudly. They asked the boy, 'But why do you ask us this odd question, boy?'

The boy replied, 'My mother has asked me to spend time with gentlemen, sirs, so that I can become one, too.'

The robbers, struck by this strange young man, consulted with each other and decided to take him in; if nothing else, they could use him for one of their heists. They told the simpleton, 'You're in luck, boy, we are gentlemen and we will teach you everything that you ever need to learn,' and began training him to be a thief.

After some days of intensive training, the thieves decided to take the boy along for a mission. They told him, 'Boy, what you will do tonight is very important for any gentleman to learn. We will enter a house and you must find the heaviest thing you can carry and bring it out.'

The boy said, 'All right, sirs, I will do as you say.'

That night they broke into a house. The thieves all scattered to find various articles of value. The boy, in the dim light, felt his way around the house and came to the kitchen. There he saw the large *janto*, grindstone, and picked it up. The janto was, by far, the heaviest thing in the house. Elated, he took it to the hideout. When the thieves gathered, everyone pulled out the precious articles they had gathered. The boy, too, proudly pulled out the grindstone.

In shock, one thief asked the boy, 'But why did you bring this grindstone, fool?'

The boy replied simply, 'Sir, I only followed your orders and brought the heaviest thing I could carry.'

The robbers all fell about laughing. Then, one of them told the simpleton, 'Boy, next time, try and find something that makes a sound, for example, a tinkle, when you pick it up.'

Some days later they raided another house. As before, the thieves scattered to find the best things to steal. The simpleton, with only one thing on his mind, kept looking. In the dim light he stumbled upon a *damaha*, a percussion instrument, which made quite a racket. The object, though it made no tinkle, was the best thing to take away. They gathered at their hideout and began to count the spoils from the night's expedition. When the boy took the *damaha* out, the robbers were shocked. One asked, 'But why did you bring this damaha, boy?'

The boy replied, 'But, Sir, you told me to find something that makes noise.'

Faced with this piece of logic, the thieves fell silent. One

The Simpleton

of the thieves said to the boy, 'The next time, you must look for something that shines, or, at least, glows in the dark.'

A few days later, the gang raided yet another house. As per his brief, the boy went looking for things that glowed. He searched all over but found nothing. In the kitchen, the lady of the house had left a pot of milk on the stove to cool. It was the only thing in the entire house which glowed, however slightly, in the dark. The simpleton picked it up, but the pot had not cooled enough. His hands burned and he dropped the vessel. The clatter of the falling vessel alerted the robbers who vanished into the night. It also woke up the owner of the house who quickly nabbed the boy.

The owner severely beat the boy and threatened to hand him over to the authorities. But the boy only wept and kept repeating that he was only doing what his gentlemen masters had told him to do. The boy was making no sense and instead of looking for precious things in the house, he had tried to steal milk. The house owner decided that this boy was some kind of fool and not worth wasting time over. He kicked him out.

The thieves had deserted him and the boy had no option but to go home. When he reached home, the boy told his mother all that had happened. He made her promise that she would never send him to other gentlemen ever again. The widow cursed her fate for having given birth to such a fool.

The more he stayed at home, the more the boy's mother tired of him. She decided that the only way out was to get him married. Having a wife would teach him to be responsible in a hurry. She told him, 'Son, you must get married.' But being the fool that he was, the simpleton asked his mother, 'But how do I get a wife?' Just barely stopping herself from hitting her forehead in frustration, the widow replied, 'Go to the village spring, son, and wait for a young girl. Whistle at her and if she does not look at you, toss a pebble at her. She will turn, and then you can speak to her.'

The boy happily went to the communal spring. There, a pretty girl was collecting water. He whistled at her, and even called out to her, but she knew who it was who was doing the whistling and did not respond. He was angered and threw a rock at the girl. The rock hit her on the head and she died on the spot. Terrfied, the simpleton quickly took the dead body to a nearby forest and buried it. He then came home and told his mother what had happened.

It was evident that the disappearance would be investigated. She asked her son where he had buried the body. Taking exact directions from the simpleton, she went to the forest and exhumed the body. Replacing the body with a dead goat, she threw the dead girl into the river.

When she came home, the widow told the simpleton to sit in the courtyard, for it would soon rain *furaulas*, a popular light snack. The boy sat expectantly and his mother hurriedly prepared furaulas and began throwing them from the veranda. The boy picked up the snacks and began eating them with great relish.

A few days later, the girl's father arrived with *praharis*, policemen. They were conducting routine enquiries. When asked if the simpleton had seen the girl, the boy replied that not only had he seen the girl, he had thrown the rock which killed her. The girl's father and the policemen were shocked. They then asked the boy when he had killed the girl. The boy replied, 'I killed her on the day it rained furaulas.' The investigators were surprised. But they persisted with the investigation and asked the boy to take them to the place he had buried the body. The boy readily agreed. He took them to the forest and began digging. But, as he groped about, he came upon a tail.

He asked the father, 'Did your daughter have a tail?'

The father angrily replied, 'No, why don't you stop wasting our time and keep digging?'

As he dug further, the boy encountered a horn. He asked the father, 'Did your daughter have horns?'

The boy's impertinence angered the father so much that he shoved him aside and began digging. When he uncovered the dead goat, he became convinced that they were dealing with a congenital fool. They walked away cursing the boy for all the time he had wasted.

His mother, on the other hand, was pleased with her ingenuity and was now convinced that if she did not take matters into her own hands, the boy would amount to nothing. She then sent a marriage proposal to a formerly wealthy family who had fallen on rough times. The family, eyeing the widow's evident wealth, agreed to the match.

The marriage soon took place. Some months later, the bride went home and did not come back for many days. The widow asked her son to go to his in-laws' and fetch his wife; she was having trouble running the house on her own. The boy said that he was afraid to take the road to his in-laws'; it passed through a forest and there were wild animals. His mother reassured him that nothing bad would happen to him if he kept making noises and throwing pebbles and stones into the forest and undergrowth.

The boy left and walked along the road, singing, loudly and skipping stones. A hunter was taking careful aim at a deer grazing nearby and the boy spooked the animal. The hunter caught the boy by the ear and gave him a sound thrashing. Crying in pain and humiliation, the boy walked on. Near his wife's village, he fell in with a marriage procession. Some drunken louts, who were with the marriage party, fell on him and beat him up, angry that he was crying on a joyous occasion. He was forced to laugh and keep laughing till he reached his destination. As he walked to his in-law's house, he came across a funeral procession. The people in the procession took exception to his good humour and roughed him up for being merry at a death march.

When he reached his wife's house, he was tired, hungry and much bruised. His face was swollen but when his father-in-law asked if all was well, he replied that it was only a minor fall. A lavish spread had been prepared for the son-in-law but the boy could not eat well, partly from the way his body was hurting but more because his mother had asked him to be sparing lest his in-laws made fun of his gluttony. He was also coached by his mother to make polite conversation. And to everything his father-in-law said, he was only to shake his head and say, 'Yes, yes.' The father-in-law told him that he was going through a bad patch: a prize goat and his best buffalo had died a some time ago. The boy kept nodding his head and saying, 'Yes, yes.' Thinking that the fall had perhaps unsettled the son-in-law, the old man said nothing. And, in any case, all eccentricities of a rich son-in-law have to be endured. After dinner the boy was shown his pallet.

He had not eaten well and by midnight, began feeling hungry. He stealthily went to the kitchen and began quickly stuffing his mouth with leftovers from the day. In his haste, he dropped a vessel which woke his father-in-law. He ran to the kitchen and saw the boy standing in evident distress, his cheeks hugely swollen by all the food he'd stuffed.

Father-in-law said, 'Son, it looks like the fall you had was more serious than we thought. If we don't do something about it, your cheeks will burst because of the swelling. But don't worry, I know a remedy. If the skin is slightly nicked with a razor, the swelling will subside.' And then he rushed off. Afraid that he would be cut, the boy ran away and was never heard of again.

The Simpleton

How the Newari New Year Began

In 880 AD, the Kathmandu valley was divided into two parts, Bhadgaon and Kathmandu. Bhadgaon was ruled by Ananda Malla, while his brother, Jaya Dev Malla, ruled Kathmandu.

Siddhiwanta, a learned and famous man, was court astrologer for Ananda Malla. One day, in the course of his research in astrology, Siddhiwanta found that if sand from the Lakhu Tirtha river in Kathmandu was to be picked up at a certain time in the morning on a particular date, it would turn to gold. The astrologer was very excited with this find and told his king.

The king had a very high opinion of his astrologer and full faith in his abilities. He summoned four of his strongest, most able soldiers and told them that they were to go to Kathmandu in secret on the date and time specified, and no later, and were to bring back as much sand as they could carry from the Lakhu Tirtha river. The four soldiers made it into Kathmandu without mishap and managed to collect the sand. On their way back to Bhadgaon, the soldiers ran into Shankhadhar. Shankhadhar was suspicious of these men who did not look like they were from Kathmandu; their manner of speech suggested they were from Bhadgaon. He asked them, 'Where are you from, brothers?' One of the soldiers, understanding that their accents had given them away, replied, 'Bhadgaon.'

Shankhadhar enquired further, 'But, brothers, you have a river in Bhadgaon, and sand, what need do you have for our sand?'

The soldiers had not been told what the sand was for. So they quite candidly replied that they were only following orders and knew nothing of what it was to be used for. Shankhadhar suspected something amiss. There was no earthly reason why the king of Bhadgaon should need sand from Kathmandu. He said to the soldiers, 'Brothers, this sand is wet and heavy, and you must be tired. You are our guests; please come with me to my house.' Impressed by this good-natured, hospitable man, the soldiers went to his house. There, he treated the soldiers to some excellent food and homemade *raksi*, liquor. When it was time for the soldiers to leave, Shankhadhar said to them, 'I myself have been intending to go to the river to fetch some sand. Since you have so kindly brought the sand to my house, I was hoping you could leave it behind and save me the trouble of going to the river. You can always pick up more sand from further on; that really would save you a lot of trouble.' In the spirit of bonhomie created by the raksi, the soldiers readily agreed. They took their leave and picked up sand from another place in the river to take to Ananda Malla.

Shankhadhar's hunch was proved right: the sand the soldiers had left behind soon turned to gold. His joy knew no bounds. He went straight to his king, Jaya Dev Malla, and told him about the change in his fortunes. He added that it was only right that his fortune, which he had come across by chance, should be shared with one and all. He offered to pay the debts of all the citizens in Kathmandu. Jaya Dev Malla, only too glad to have one less thing to worry about, made the announcement that everyone was to declare their debts so that Shankhadhar could pay them off.

That day, Ananda Malla eagerly went to the vault in which the precious sand was kept. None of it had turned into gold. He summoned Siddhiwanta and asked him why the sand remained the same. Siddhiwanta, despite his extensive knowledge of astrology, had no answer. Ananda Malla severely reprimanded the astrologer and sent him home. When he reached home, Siddhiwanta was so stricken by the royal disapproval and the failure of his prediction that he burnt the book of astrology he consulted and fell off into a dead faint. His wife panicked and did not know what to do. As she rushed out to find help, she almost came under the wheels of the royal chariot that was pulling into their courtyard. She fell at the king's feet and implored him to save her husband.

The king came in and asked Siddhiwanta's wife to light a couple of incense sticks. He then put the incense sticks under Siddhiwanta's nose and he soon revived. The king said to him, 'You must forgive me for doubting you, Siddhiwanta. I later checked both the baskets of sand and there was gold dust stuck to the bottom.'

Siddhiwanta said, 'Your Highness, something about this does not seem right. The guards who went to fetch the sand must be questioned.'

Just as Siddhiwanta spoke, a guard arrived with a note from Jaya Dev Malla. Reading it aloud, Ananda Malla described how Shankhadhar had become very rich and intended to pay back the debts of all the people in the

Kathmandu valley. Ananda was to collect information on how much the total debt of the kingdom actually was and send it to Jaya Dev. This was indeed great news; the wealth that had been collected was being put to good use. The date on which the valley's debts were cleared has, since then, been celebrated as the Newari new year.

How the Newari New Year Began

The Saintly Falcon

A falcon was growing old and could no longer easily catch prey. He had gone without food for three days and, not having enough energy to fly, was perched on the branch of a tree growing on a hillside and was surveying the landscape with keen eyes for things to eat. All of a sudden, he spotted some rats scurrying about in front of a hole. He was tempted to swoop down and catch one for a quick meal but stopped. The falcon realized that if he caught even one rat, the rest would be spooked and would never use that particular exit again. However, if he used his brain, he could work things out and ensure a regular, easy food supply for himself. The falcon was clever and soon enough, hit upon an idea.

When there weren't any rats around, he flew down to the burrow exit, stood on one leg and looked at the sun. A rat saw the falcon as he was coming out of the hole and ran back inside in fright. He told his friends about the strange spectacle. Curious, the rats came out of the hole and, from a safe distance, asked the falcon what he was doing. He said that he was a great devotee of the sun and was thus paying tribute. The falcon added that it was his intention to keep standing like this without eating anything for the rest of his life. The rats were impressed with this saintly falcon who was confident that he could survive on nothing. They believed that if they visited him at least once a day, all their sins would be washed away. This was perfect for the falcon; every time the rats came out, he would strike poses and spout all manners of nonsense. But when the rats trooped back into their hole, he would pluck off a straggler. As days went by, the number of rats dropped and this became a matter of concern. The king of rats convened a meeting but it soon became apparent that no one knew anything. All the king understood was that the disappearances coincided with the arrival of the saintly falcon. He decided to investigate the matter.

The next day the king went out with other rats. After darshan, the king rat decided to be the last to enter. The falcon tried to snatch the king but he was ready for it. He raised an alarm and the rats rushed to the aid of their monarch and bit the saintly falcon to death.

The Boon

Losey Ram was an honest and diligent man, a devotee of Lord Ganesh, desperately poor and not, as his name suggests, slow. He was a very simple man and everyone would try to exploit him in some way or the other. Every day, before he ate anything, he would pay a visit to the Ganesh temple which was situated at some distance from his village. Ganesh was pleased with Losey's unstinting devotion and decided to give him darshan. One day, when Losey opened his eyes, he found Lord Ganesh standing in front of him. He told Losey Ram, 'I am pleased with you. Ask for whatever you want.' Losey was content with his life and told Ganesh that he did not want anything. But Ganesh insisted and so Losey told the god that he would first consult with his wife and mother and see if they wanted anything. Lord Ganesh gave him some time.

Losey Ram went home and spoke with his wife. The couple was childless and his wife dearly wanted a son. So she told Losey that he should ask Ganesh for a male child. He then spoke with his mother. She was a practical woman

and knew that a grandson would only mean an added drain on the meagre resources of the family. So she told Losey Ram to ask for an unending supply of food.

Losey Ram was confused and did not know what he should ask. On his way back to the temple, he was deep in thought. He walked past Chattu Ram, a smart man but a drunkard, without a word of greeting. Chattu was intrigued and stopped Losey to ask what was bothering him. Losey told Chattu about the boon and the difficulty he faced in choosing. Chattu Ram found it difficult to believe that Lord Ganesh would ever appear to anyone. But Losey was nothing if not honest and had always been known to all as a staunch devotee of Lord Ganesh. He decided, since he had nothing better to do, to help Losey. He thought for a moment and then whispered something in Losey's ear. Losey took Chattu's statement to be very clever and happily went to the temple.

Lord Ganesh appeared again and asked, 'Have you decided on anything?'

'Yes,' said Losey Ram. 'Since you insist that I must ask for something, I would request you to make me lucky enough to see my son playing with different toys, under the care of many maids, and my wife and mother, very pleased at the sight, spend time talking with each other in the veranda of a beautiful house eating the most sumptuous food.'

Lord Ganesh laughed and then asked Losey, 'Did you come up with this yourself, Losey?' Ever truthful, Losey replied, 'I could never have thought up something so clever by myself. Chattu Ram taught me to say all this to you.' Lord Ganesh explained to Losey that Chattu had rolled many boons into one and while he could not refuse the boon to Losey, Chattu Ram deserved punishment. He granted Losey his wish, but said, 'May Chattu Ram never have enough money for liquor,' and vanished.

The Story of a Jacket

An old Newar couple lived in a village in Bhaktapur. They were poor farmers leading, mostly, a hand-to-mouth existence. But the old Newar man had one extraordinary skill: he knew the cure for sore eyes. He was known all over Bhaktapur, and beyond, for this gift.

One morning, as the Newar was going to the fields he sharecropped, he was stopped by a Brahmin. The Brahmin asked the Newar to come with him; his wife was suffering greatly because of her eyes.

The Newar said, 'But, Sir, today I need to unblock the water channels in my fields. It will take me all morning and I can come only later in the day, maybe only by evening.'

But the Brahmin implored, 'Newar, my wife is in great discomfort. Please come with me right away. I will give you anything you ask for.' After some hesitation, the Newar agreed.

They walked for many hours before reaching Taudaha lake. There, the Brahmin turned and told the astonished Newar that he was Karkotak, the god of snakes. His palace,

and his ailing wife were underneath the lake. The Brahmin refused to believe this, so Karkotak turned into a snake to prove that he was telling the truth. He then convinced the alarmed Brahmin to lie down beside the lake and close his eyes. When the Brahmin opened his eyes, he found himself in a magnificent room in what seemed like a huge palace. The snake-queen sat on a bed, her eyes red and streaming. The Brahmin inspected her eyes and asked for a glass of water. He began reciting some prayers. When he had finished uttering the mantras, he rubbed the skin behind his right ear and washed his fingers in the glass of water and chanted some more prayers. He then applied the water on the queen's eyes. The treatment, continued over a period of five days, completely cured the snake-queen's eyes.

Karkotak was overjoyed. He asked the Newar to demand anything he wanted. In the five days he had lived at the palace, the Newar had been living a good, comfortable life. He had been shown around the beautiful palace by Karkotak himself and there was one thing that he liked above everything else: a jacket Karkotak was wearing that was beautifully embroidered with gold thread and studded with precious gems. He asked Karkotak if he could have the jacket as his reward. The snake-king happily took the jacket off and gave it to the Newar. He had only one condition. He said, 'Newar, I am extremely glad, and infinitely relieved that you have cured my wife. I am gladly handing over this jacket to you. But remember, this is a sacred and precious jacket; you must never give this away nor must you ever tell anyone how it came into your possession.' The Newar agreed. He was then asked to close his eyes and lie down. When he opened them again, the Newar found himself in the exact spot he had met the Brahmin. For a moment, he thought he had been dreaming but when he saw the jacket he was wearing, he was instantly convinced. Taking it off, he hid the precious jacket underneath the other clothes he was wearing and rushed home.

As soon as his wife saw him, she began to screech at the Newar. She had been worried sick and had given up looking for him. Now, she was preparing herself for a life of widowhood without even being sure that her husband was truly dead. The Newar somehow calmed his wife down and told her of his adventure. She didn't believe him, attributing his story to some drunken binge. But when he showed her the jacket, she believed him.

The Newar became obsessed with his jewel-studded jacket. At home, he never took it off and even when he went to the fields, he would take his jacket along, folded and carefully packed. One day, a ghost was crossing the field the Newar was working in. He saw the carefully folded packet and opened it. When he saw the beautiful jacket, the ghost knew it had to possess it. He changed his form into that of a human being, went up to the Newar and told him that he knew that in the packet was a beautiful jacket for which the Newar must name his price. The Newar was shocked that his secret had so easily come out into the open and he refused to part with the jacket at any price. The ghost went away, disappointed.

The next day, the ghost returned, intending to steal the jacket. When the Newar's back was turned he quickly picked up the jacket and ran away. The Newar saw the thief and gave chase but his old legs could hardly catch up with a ghost. He then went home dejected and told his wife about his misfortune but she only scolded him for his foolhardiness.

That evening, the third night of the chariot festival of Karunamaya, which is celebrated in the month of Jyeshta, was being observed. Many people had gathered in Jawalakhel for the festival. Some were chanting hymns and reading scriptures. Others were lighting *diyos* around the chariot. Still others were playing music. Karkotak, disguised as a human being, had also come to Jawalakhel and so had the Newar from Bhaktapur, who was attending the festival to pray for the return of his precious jacket. Some ghosts, including the one that had stolen the jacket, had gathered at Jawalakhel. It was a place with a lot of traffic and there were plenty of opportunities for mischief. They made food disappear as well as the offerings people had brought with them. A Vajracharya was asked why the food was disappearing. He suspected this to be the mischief of the ghosts. He uttered some mantras which made the ghosts both visible and immobile. The Newar saw the ghost wearing his jacket and tried to snatch it off him. The ghost steadfastly refused and stuck to his story that he had found the jacket in a field. As the argument heated, people gathered around to watch the spectacle. Karkotak too came to see what was happening.

When he saw that it was his jacket that was creating all this trouble, he stepped forward and revealed his true identity to all the people present there; once even changing form. Karkotak then asked the ghost to hand the jacket over to the Newar. But the ghost refused, saying, 'I stole the jacket so it cannot be mine; but the Newar too does not deserve the jacket. For him, the jacket became everything and he failed to recognize its true worth. Therefore, I propose that the jacket should be offered to Karunamaya.' When the Newar saw that he could not win, he agreed.

Then, with Karkotak leading the way, everyone went to the chariot. There, Karkotak held up the jacket and announced in a loud voice: 'Let the king come to the festival on this day every year and let the jacket of the king of serpents be shown in three different directions. First, for the benefit of the gods, people and serpent. Second, for the benefit of the people living in Yen, Yela, Khopa and Taudah, and respected teacher Bandhudatta, king Narendradeva and farmer Rathchakra. And, third, for the benefit of the ghost, the farmer and Vajracharya.' With this announcement, Karkotak disappeared from sight. From that day on, the jacket is displayed during the chariot festival.

The Story of a Jacket

The Millet Bread

A family of three lived in the mountains of Nepal. The parents were farmers and tried very hard to eke a living out of the stony soil but never had enough. Their son, though a young, strapping lad, was exceedingly lazy. He dreamt of the day he would become rich and famous. Whenever his parents asked him to do any work, he would just ignore them.

The parents finally tired of their lazy son and, one day, sat down with him. They told him that it was not possible to carry on in this fashion. He would have to go away and not come back till he had found a way to make a living, or at least, till he had earned something of value. His mother handed him three *rotis* made of millet and bid him goodbye. The boy now had no option but to leave.

He took to the road at first light of day and walked until noon, when he came to a *chautari* where a huge banyan tree offered shade. He sat on the chautari and took out the packet of rotis his mother had packed. He was faced with a dilemma and he thought aloud, 'I am hungry enough to eat all three but I think it would be prudent to save a couple for later.'

Underneath the tree there was a cave and a family of giants lived in it. That day, the giantess was alone with her three children. She heard the boy think out aloud and assumed that he was talking about eating her three children. This must indeed be a powerful being if he could talk so openly about feeding on giants' children. She decided that a truce was better than confrontation. The giantess came out of the cave and implored the astonished and terrified boy not to eat her children. But her tone of voice soon made the boy realize that there was some confusion. He decided to take advantage of the situation. He asked the giantess, 'What can you give me in return for your children, giantess?'

The giantess replied, 'If you spare my children's lives, sir, I will give you a nanny-goat that drops gold pellets.' She then conjured up a beautiful goat which she gave the boy. The boy was very happy. He would go home and give his parents the goat and they would never nag him about his laziness again. He hoisted the goat on to his shoulders and began walking home. But the goat was heavy and he was tired. It soon became dark. The boy decided to stay the night at his uncle's house.

His uncle, surprised to see the boy carrying a goat, let him into the house. He uncle was curious: how was his nephew, notorious for laziness, doing any work at all? He told the boy, 'Nephew, this is a beautiful goat; where did you get it from?' The boy was still dazed by his good luck and soon came out with the whole story. His uncle expressed great wonder and congratulated the boy on his good fortune. They had an early dinner and went to bed. At night, the uncle replaced the magical goat with an identical one from his herd.

The next day, the boy left early, eager to show off his new-found treasure to his parents. When he reached home, he called his parents out into the courtyard and bragged much about how he had outwitted a giantess and made her give him a miraculous goat. His parents were very excited and waited for the goat to do its work. But all that the goat did was drop its usual pellets. This earned the boy a fierce slap across the face.

The boy spent that day sulking at home and early next morning, he went back to the giantess' cave. He stood at the chautari and shouted in the loudest voice possible, 'Giantess, tell me, how many of your children should I eat to repay your trickery?'

The Millet Bread

The giantess rushed out. She was contrite and told the boy, 'The goat should have given you gold, sir. But never mind, if you spare my children, I will give you a *gamcha*, a towel, which will produce a feast every time you lay it on the ground.' She then conjured up the magical gamcha and showed the boy how to get food from it.

The boy when away happily. But it soon became dark and he had to go to his uncle's house for the night. His uncle was again surprised to see his nephew turn up late in the evening and that, too, with a towel. He welcomed the boy and asked him what he was doing with a towel. The entire story came tumbling out and the uncle again expressed wonder at his nephew's great fortune. That night, the boy's uncle replaced the magical towel with an identical one from his cupboard.

The next morning, the boy hurried home with his magical towel. He called his parents out to the courtyard and said that he would make them regret their earlier outburst. He spread the towel on the ground and uttered the magical words. But even though he tried every inflection and tone of voice, the gamcha remained empty. His father again slapped him and said that if he pulled another prank again, he would get a thorough hiding.

The next afternoon, he reached the giantess' cave and angrily shouted, 'Giantess, you have twice deceived me, I must eat at least one of your children to teach you a lesson.'

The giantess hastily came outside and said to the boy, 'Sir, you saw for yourself the goat producing gold and the towel producing food. Where do you go after you leave here?'

When the boy replied that he stopped over at his uncle's house on his way back, the giantess suspected that the boy was being taken for a ride. She said to the boy, 'Sir, for sparing my children, I will give you a wand. You must take it to your uncle and tell him that come what may, he must never utter the words, "Hit me," near it. He will certainly say these words and when the wand is beating him up, make him give you the goat and the towel.'

The boy replied, 'If this wand of yours works, I will give up any thoughts of making a meal of your children. But remember, if you have tricked me, nothing can save them from me.'

The giantess reassured him that he was not being tricked and the boy went to his uncle's house, showing off the wand. His expressed great surprise at the fact that his nephew was keeping exceptionally busy these days. He asked what the beautifully polished wand was for; was nephew learning magic these days? The boy replied, 'Yes, uncle, I am. And, I am keeping this wand here. Under no circumstances must we utter the words, "Hit me," while holding it.' So saying, the boy fell asleep.

The boy had been bringing some wonderful articles home; perhaps this wand was the best of the lot. In the dead of the night the uncle crept up to the wand and holding it expectantly in his right hand, said firmly, 'Hit me.' The wand took on a life of its own and began raining blows on the uncle's back and legs. His cries alerted the boy who rushed out. He saw uncle running around frantically and the wand following him, trying to find the tenderest spots on his body.

He said, 'Uncle, if you don't tell me what you did with my towel and goat, I will allow this wand to beat you to death.'

Uncle howled with pain but denied doing anything, so he just sat back and enjoyed the beating his uncle was receiving. Eventually, uncle screamed, 'Nephew, I switched your magical goat and towel for ordinary ones. Call this wand off and I will tell you where to find them.' The boy agreed and told the wand to stop beating his uncle.

He took the miraculous goat and towel home and called his parents out. But they were fed up with his pranks and stayed inside. He then went inside with the towel and the goat, and, despite the protestations of his mother, tied up the animal to a bedpost. He then spread the gamcha on the ground and conjured up the most amazing feast for all. In the meanwhile, the goat, which had been idly chewing on a corner of the bedspread, dropped a score of golden pellets. Forced to believe the evidence of their eyes, the boy's parents were exceedingly happy with their son and never complained about his laziness.

The Millet Bread

Selfishness

A rich widower was the owner of much land and many head of cattle. He lived fairly happily with his two sons, their wives and grandchildren. He was the head of his family and worked hard at overseeing the work in the fields as well as at home and ensured that money always flowed in. One day, he decided that he was getting old and had worked enough. He called in his sons and divided the property and the responsibility of overseeing work on the farm and at home equally between the two. He then announced that he would divide his time between the families of his two sons.

The first year passed wonderfully. He lived for six months with each son and had no care in the world. His sons were capable and he had taught them well. His daughters-in-law, too, were careful to obey his every wish and took great care of him. He renewed his old contacts and spent much time with his grandchildren, and did social work. However, with passing time, things changed. The constant presence of the father at home, and the fact that he did nothing, began to bother the sons. Their wives too were irritated with the added responsibility. Issues about who would host father, and for how long, became bones of contention. The old widower began to detect a distinct coldness in his sons' and their wives' treatment of him. His daughters-in-law did not pay any attention to his food and would keep him waiting for even minor things like tea. Worse, they served him stale food. His sons ignored him and even the grandchildren became rude.

The widower, in his wildest dreams, had not expected that such a fate could befall him. One day, unable to keep his tribulations to himself, he told the village priest, a very close friend, his story. The priest was indignant and distressed about the way his friend was being treated by his own flesh and blood. He understood human nature very well and knew that the widower was being mistreated because the sons and their families stood to gain nothing more from him. He devised a plan: the widower was to empty one of the big, imposing chests he had and fill it up with rocks. He was then to securely lock the chest up and keep it in his room, pretending that it contained something of great value. The more the widower thought about this plan, the more it attracted him. He decided to give it a shot.

That evening, he made a great show of not coming out to eat; he kept his door locked and used the time he had to empty and prepare the chest. His children were intrigued. Then he told his daughter-in-law that he would not be eating with the rest of the family but would like to be served dinner in his bedroom. And when she was laying out the dinner on his table, he pretended to watch her with keen eyes, as though he suspected her every move. When the daughter-in-law came out, she told her husband about his father's strange behaviour and the two discussed that father must have something to hide; something he did not want them to know about and something he obviously did not want to share. The two drew the conclusion that it could only be treasure of some sort.

When the widower moved to his other son's house, he got his son to lug the heavy box to his house. There, too, he created a great mystery about the box, pretending to suspect everyone who even came close to it. As his friend, the priest, had predicted, he started being treated better. His meals were on time and they were always freshly cooked. His sons, whenever they could, made small talk with him and his grandchildren were courteous and attentive. Both families vied with each other to get into his good books. And the old widower lived in great comfort, albeit with some dissembling, till the day he died. Before he died, he told his sons that they must share equally whatever was in the box.

The sons decided to open the box together and when they did, found nothing but rocks and stones in it. They were very disappointed and angry at being duped like this. However, when they thought about what their father had done, it struck them that it was their behaviour that had driven him to it. Father, from his deathbed, had taught them a lesson about selfishness that they would never forget.

The Farmer's Victory

On a hot, dry Asar day, Mahadev, the god of gods, and his consort Parvati were on earth, disguised as humans. They saw a farmer diligently tilling his land which was bone dry. Seeing the man put so much effort into a seemingly futile exercise, Mahadev asked, 'Why are you working in this heat?'

The man replied, 'I am preparing to sow paddy.'

Mahadev laughed, 'And why do you think any paddy will grow in this parched land?'

The man said, 'It will rain in the evening.'

Mahadev looked up at the sky. The sun beat down fiercely and not a single cloud could be seen. But the farmer seemed certain and so Mahadev asked, 'Do you really think it will rain today?'

'It will.'

Mahadev was intrigued, 'How can you say that it will rain?'

'It just will.'

The farmer could give no credible reason why it would rain but his faith, though blind, was solid. This irked Mahadev

and he felt that the farmer should be taught a lesson. Mahadev asked the farmer to a wager of one gold coin which he accepted.

Mahadev, though sure it would not rain, still decided to make certain that he would win the bet. He went up to Lord Indra, the god of rain, to ask him not to send down any rain on earth that day. 'I will not send any rain today,' said Indra, 'but I cannot do anything if the frogs start to sing the rain song. So you better go to them and ask them not to sing their in the evening.' Mahadev then descended to earth and told the frogs, 'I am Mahadev, the god of gods. I order you not to sing the rain song today.' The frogs said, 'We will obey your order but there is a problem: we cannot prevent ourselves from singing if the fireflies start to flash their lights. You better go to the fireflies and ask them to keep their lights doused.' Mahadev then ordered the fireflies to not flash their lights. They said they wouldn't and Mahadev went to his abode on Mount Kailash sure it wouldn't rain that day.

The farmer kept peering at the sky for signs of rain; there was not a cloud to be seen. Daylight waned and evening came on and there was still no rain. The farmer became slightly worried. If it did not rain, all his hard work would be wasted, and worse, the soil which he had loosened could also be blown away by the wind; the bet he had waged with the stranger that day was far from his mind. He lit a torch and went out into the fields; if it rained tonight, he would have to be at hand to control the flow of water. A frog, from a distance, mistook the approaching torch for the glow of a firefly and began to croak the rain song. The song was taken up by all the frogs and soon rose up to a crescendo. Indra heard the song and had no option but to send the rain down.

When Mahadev saw it was raining, he berated Indra for not keeping his word. Indra replied that he had already warned Mahadev that he could hold the rain back only as long as the frogs did not croak their rain song. If anything, Mahadev should take the issue up with the frogs. Mahadev went to the frogs and scolded them for disobeying his orders, but the frogs replied that they had no choice as they saw one firefly flashing its light; it was its fault. Furious, Mahadev stormed off to the fireflies who cowered under his wrath. They told him that not one of them had gone against his command and, in fact, had spent most of the night cowering under leaves because of the rain. Then, one firefly pointed at the light in the distance. If all the fireflies were present and accounted for, what was that in the distance?

Mahadev began walking towards the light. While still some distance away, he could see that the source of the light was a torch which had been set up under a makeshift shed to protect it from the rain. Nearby, he could see the farmer working furiously to channel the water to various parts of his field. He disguised himself and walked up to the farmer. The farmer, with much astonishment, accepted the one gold coin that the stranger offered him for winning the bet and went back to work. Mahadev accepted defeat and downcast, returned to Mount Kailash.

The Farmer's Victory

Keshchandra

Keshchandra lived in Itumbul in Kathmandu. He was a bachelor, and a rich man, and he had one besetting sin: he loved to gamble. Over time, Keshchandra lost all his wealth at the gambling tables until, one day, his servant came up to him and said that there was nothing left to eat in the house. He decided to go to his sister's house to see what he could do to recover his lost fortune.

Keshchandra's sister welcomed him and served him delicious food on a golden platter. He ate all of it and when his sister had stepped out of the room, quickly walked away with the gold plate. He reasoned that he could pawn the plate and gamble with the money. And with his winnings, he could get the plate back. He pawned the plate, gambled, and lost all the money.

The next morning, Keshchandra went back to his sister's house. She pretended not to have noticed the disappearance of the gold plate and served her brother breakfast on a silver plate. Keshchandra suffered from a chronic case of over-confidence. He stole the silver plate, pawned it, gambled, and promptly lost the money. By lunchtime, he was back at his sister's house.

She again pretended not to have noticed her lost cutlery. She then asked Keshchandra to sit for lunch. As is customary, Keshchandra sat cross-legged on the floor. His sister then carefully washed the floor in front of him and served him food on it. She then went out. Keshchandra, feeling very humiliated, carefully gathered all the food in his handkerchief and rushed out without saying anything to his sister.

He walked for hours, raging against his fate. By evening he felt tired and hungry. He stopped and opened the packet but the food reminded him of the humiliation he had been subjected to. He walked on till night fell but he still couldn't eat the food. That night, he went to sleep hungry. The next morning, when he woke up, he was famished. He decided to swallow his pride and eat the food but when he opened the packet he found that the food had gone bad. He set it out in the sun to dry, hoping that he could eat at least a part of it. He went to sleep again. When he woke up, he found that a flock of pigeons had eaten every last scrap of food. He began weeping loudly, beating his breast. Seeing Keshchandra distressed, the leader of the flock, the king of pigeons, pitied him and ordered his flock to repay the man. The birds flew over to Keshchandra and shat all around him. At first, Keashchandra was shocked and disgusted but on carefully examining the droppings, he found that they were all gold. He thanked the birds and gathered all the gold in one place. There was much gold and it was very heavy. Just as Keshchandra was deciding his course of action, he heard a rumble. He looked up and saw a towering demon, with huge sabre-like tusks, claws and a hairy body bounding towards him.

Keshchandra, although frightened, gathered courage and said, 'Who may you be, noble demon?'

The demon replied, 'I am Gurumappa, and I am hungry for human flesh. It is indeed a happy coincidence that I should find you here.'

Keshchandra, still keeping his cool, said, 'Noble Gurumappa, I am a mere morsel, and if you eat me today, I will only momentarily satisfy your hunger. But if you let me live, I will provide for you one buffalo and as much rice as you can eat, every day, for as long as I live. But, right now, you must help me carry all this gold home.'

Gurumappa helped Keshchandra, and he began to keep

his end of the bargain. Things were smooth for a while, but trouble erupted when children began to disappear. The citizens of Itumbul went to Keshchandra and requested him to get Gurumappa to move to Tundikhel on the outskirts of the valley. For this, they would feed Gurumappa even after Keshchandra was gone.

Gurumappa agreed, and to this day, the people of Itumbul keep him happy by offering him buffalo meat and rice every year.

The Frog

A childless, unhappy couple were great devotees of Lord Vishnu and had made every pilgrimage possible in the hope of a child. After years of penance and tramping up and down temple stairs, the wife conceived. The couple was overjoyed and could hardly wait for nine months. But when the baby finally came, they were shocked to see that the baby was not human but a frog. The father was so disappointed that he asked his wife to go out and leave the child at some crossroads. But mothers are blind to the faults of their children. She decided that she would raise the frog as her own. The frog grew up like any human child and learnt human speech well.

Father would go every day to the fields. At noon, mother took him lunch. One day, mother had urgent work to attend to and could not find time to reach father his lunch. She was desperately looking for someone to take him his food when the frog came in and said that he would do it. Mother was not sure the frog could carry the food but he convinced her. She tied the food into a bundle and the bundle to a stick, making it easier for him to carry it. When he reached

the fields, father seemed pleased to see him, one of the few times that he was happy with his frog-son. Thereafter, the frog always took food for his father and even helped mother with minor household chores.

It bothered the frog that his parents worked so hard but never had enough. So one day he told his father that he should go to the king and ask him for a few cattle. Father laughed and said to his son, 'But why would the king give us anything just because we are poor? There are thousands of poor families in the kingdom; the king cannot go around giving cattle to all!' But his frog-son insisted, 'You can try once, can't you?' But father resisted the idea. The frog decided there was no other option; he would have to do something himself.

He walked to the palace and requested the king to give his father cattle. The king was initially struck by the novelty of a speaking frog and did give him a hearing. When asked why he thought the farmer needed to be given cattle, the frog replied, 'Your Highness, my parents are simple, hard-working farmers who never have enough to eat. If given a few cattle, they would be able to live comfortable lives.'

The king laughed loudly. He told the frog that if he were to give away cattle and land to all his subjects, the national coffers would be emptied in no time at all. Seeing the king laugh, the court ministers and jesters joined in and jeered the frog. Humiliated, the frog walked away.

The next morning, the cows and the buffaloes in the royal stables stopped giving milk. The king summoned the court astrologer and asked him to divine the cause behind the cattle's refusal to supply milk. The astrologer made his calculations and told the king that the cows and buffalos had dried up because someone had been turned away from the palace empty-handed and disappointed. The frog immediately sprang to the king's mind. He had him called to the palace and gave him the cattle he had requested. As soon as he gave the order, the cattle in the royal stables began giving more milk than ever before.

The frog's parents were very pleased to receive the cows and buffaloes from the king and thanked their son greatly. Their gratitude made the frog-son very happy. He became adventurous and told father that he wanted to marry the princess. His father, astonished at this hubris, refused outright. The frog had no option but to go on his own.

The frog reached the royal court and the king asked, 'So, frog, what brings you here?'

The frog replied, 'Your Highness, I come to ask you for your daughter's hand in marriage.'

The king became almost purple with rage. He shouted, 'You, frog, how dare you think of becoming my son-in-law? Guards! Throw this creature in the dungeon!'

The next morning, the staff which took care of the palace rushed up to the king and frantically told him that all the sources of water for the palace had dried up. The king summoned the astrologer who told him that it was again thwarted ambition that had caused the water supply to dry up. But, for the king, it was an impossible choice: a frog for a son-in-law or a dry, water-less palace. Finally, when it became impossible even to cook basic meals in the royal kitchen, the king had the frog brought into his presence.

He asked the frog, 'If I give you my daughter's hand in marriage, will you restore the palace's water supply?'

The frog replied, 'Yes.'

Then the king, with a long sigh, said, 'So be it.' As soon as he had said this, water began to flow. The marriage then was celebrated with great fanfare and the bride was brought home, weeping all the way.

The frog's parents were pleased to be related to the king

of the land in this way. But the princess hadn't been able to overcome the shock of having to marry a frog and could not stop her tears. Her in-laws, however, assumed that she was only weeping because she was sad to leave her parents' home.

Later, when the frog entered the nuptial chamber, the princess's sadness knew no bounds; she began to weep more than ever. But the frog simply shed his skin and a handsome young man emerged. The princess could only stare in wonder. The former frog told the princess that he was Lord Vishnu in disguise and she must never reveal his identity to anyone.

Later, at a royal event, she had to sit next to her frog-husband and stand the curious and, sometimes, openly jeering stares but could not reveal that she was Lord Vishnu's wife.

That night, when Lord Vishnu had changed into his handsome, young self, the princess took the frog skin and burnt it to ashes. The next morning, when Lord Vishnu began to look for his frog skin, his wife told him that she had set it afire. Lord Vishnu admonished the princess saying that it was impossible for him to continue inhabiting earth without his frog skin. He vanished, leaving behind a bewildered, sad princess.

Prince Dharmapal

O nce upon a time, a severe drought struck a small kingdom in Nepal. The king built a big, beautiful *dhara*, waterspout, but no water flowed. His subjects were greatly distressed and the king decided that he must do something to bring water to his country. He consulted many astrologers and eventually, one of them told the king that water would flow through the spout only when someone who had all the thirty-two *gunas*, qualities prescribed by the Hindu holy books, *shastras*, was sacrificed.

Thirty-two gunas in one person is rare and the astrologers examined all the horoscopes in the country and did not find anyone. Eventually, the search narrowed down to the palace. When they had gone through the horoscopes of all the members of the palace, they found that the prince, Dharmapal, and his wife exhibited all the thirty-two gunas the sacred book described. The king was thrown into a great dilemma. On the one hand, Dharmapal was his son, but there was no way he would sacrifice his daughter-in-law, either. But, the ministers, as well as the astrologers, told the king

that Dharmapal was the crown prince and all-important but the princess was expendable; if she died, the king could easily find a new daughter-in-law. The king, convinced by this logic, agreed.

When the prince learnt of this development, he was furious. But a royal decree was final and binding. He had no option but to run away. He told his wife, 'Pack our bags and be ready. We leave at midnight.'

She asked him, 'But, why this hurry?'

Prince Dharmapal replied, 'Wife, you have all the thirty-two gunas and the king has decided that you must die so that the country becomes prosperous again.'

The princess went white with fear. Seeing her reaction, Prince Dharmapal said, 'Do not fear, princess, while we cannot go against the king's wishes, we can run away. Be prepared, for we depart at midnight.'

That night, the couple stole out of the palace. Riding on fast horses, they put many miles between themselves and the kingdom before stopping in a clearing near a jungle. Both were exhausted and hungry. Prince Dharmapal went off to find food. He soon saw a stag and began stalking it. The animal began running away. The prince followed the animal till it entered a huge mansion. The prince followed it inside, but the stag had vanished. As he looked for the stag, an ogre suddenly attacked Prince Dharmapal. The ogre, masquerading as the stag, was looking for victims. The prince fought bravely and trapped the ogre in one of the rooms of the mansion. He brought his wife to the mansion and they began living there. He did not tell her about the ogre and imposed just one condition on the princess: she was never to enter the room in which the ogre was trapped.

One day, the prince was out hunting and his wife found the key to the ogre's room which he had left behind. She was curious to know why she had been forbidden from entering the room. When she opened the door, she saw the ogre and was frightened. She quickly shut the door. But the ogre was cunning. It said, 'Mistress, don't shut the door. I am lonely and afraid inside here. You are a noble princess; have pity on me. I do not ask to be freed, princess, sit with me, please, and give me company.' With many such sweet words and empty endearments, the ogre worked its way into a position of confidence with the princess.

Every time the prince went out to hunt, the princess would go to the ogre and spend long hours chatting. It helped her kill time. The ogre slowly began to look for a way to be free and extract revenge. One day, it told the princess, 'Noble princess, your husband is an intelligent man but he certainly is not brave. It is only through trickery that he managed to entrap me.'

The wife was indignant. She said, 'But how can you say such a thing? My husband is a noble prince. There is not an ounce of trickery in him.'

'All right,' the ogre said, 'then let him prove his bravery. You must pretend to be suffering from a serious ache which can be cured only by the application of a tigresses' milk.'

That evening, the princess pretended to be in great agony. She told her husband, 'An old ache has resurfaced. If you don't get me some tiger milk, husband, I will die of the agony.' Unable to see his wife in such pain, Prince Dharmapal immediately set out.

In the forest, he went to a tigress's den and spoke to the two cubs playing outside, 'Brothers, my wife is in great pain, can you give me a little bit of your mother's milk?'

The cubs asked him to wait. The tigress stepped out of her den and settled down to feed the cubs before leaving for her nocturnal hunt. As she began to leave, one of the cubs said, 'Mother, *kancha*, the younger one, gets very hungry when you are away. Could you leave some milk behind?' The tigress left some milk on a broad leaf and left. Dharmapal gratefully took the milk home. The next day, the princess eagerly went to the ogre and told him of her husband's bravery.

The ogre could barely hide its disappointment. Its said, 'But, noble princess, while this is a brave achievement, it could easily have been achieved with trickery.'

The princess expressed her protest and asked the ogre to set any other test. The ogre said to her, 'Princess, you must again pretend to be grievously hurting. And to cure your hurt, you must ask your husband to bring you the shavings of the tooth of a buck-toothed ogre who lives twenty miles to the north.' The princess agreed.

When Prince Dharmapal came home, she told him that she was hurting all over and could only feel better if he could get her the shavings of the tooth of a buck-toothed ogre who lived about twenty miles to the north. He was curious to know how she knew of the cure but the princess just ignored his questions and asked him to bring her the ogre's tooth. Prince Dharmapal went out in search of the ogre.

He found it in the place he had been told about, but the ogre had, at that time, assumed such enormous proportions that there was no way he could hope to vanquish it. Therefore, Prince Dharmapal jumped on to the ogre's body and began pricking it with his sword. The ogre tried to slap him away but the prince only shifted position and pricked the ogre some more. This went on till the ogre became exhausted. It said, 'Whoever it is, please stop tormenting me. I will give you whatever you want.'

The prince jumped off and told the ogre about his problem. It agreed to help him and the two went to the mansion. There, the ogre lay on the ground and rested its tusk on a window sill. The noise the ogre made was deafening, and the ogre inside the mansion panicked. Prince Dharmapal was stronger than he had assumed. He said, 'Princess, your husband is indeed brave, and he cares for you very much. You must now go and attend to the kitchen— he must be tired after all his exertions.' The princess hurried away, forgetting to lock the door behind her. The ogre stole out of the room and hid in the attic.

The princess went out to meet her husband. She was still pretending to be in great pain. Prince Dharmapal went to the ogre and shaved its tooth. He then thanked the ogre, who went away. Seemingly cured, the princess asked Prince Dharmapal to sit for dinner. Meanwhile, the ogre had crept down from the attic and poisoned Dharmapal's food. After eating the dinner, the prince started to feel unwell. He then vomited uncontrollably. All along, he was confused about his wife's strange illnesses and stranger cures, but the clarity of death explained everything: she had been trying to kill him. Cursing her with his last breath, he died.

The princess did not know what had happened and began to weep. Her keening wails told the ogre that its plan had succeeded. Assuming his most menacing aspect, it went to the room in which the princess was mourning. It dismembered Prince Dharmapal and ate everything of him, leaving only the heart. It threw the heart at the shocked princess, cruelly telling her that the only part of her dead husband she deserved was the heart she had broken. The princess, not knowing what to do, took the heart to a river and set it afloat.

The river took the heart downstream till it reached a *ghat* where a noblewoman was meditating. When she opened her eyes, she saw a strange and wondrous sight. A human heart floated on the river surface, and was pushed around by the eddies, but refused to drown. She asked her maids to fetch it, but the heart floated away. She then waded into the river and the heart kept circling her before she finally managed to catch it. The heart looked fresh, as though it had been lately torn out of some breast. She wrapped up the heart in a white cloth and took it home, intending to burn it on a pyre.

That night, Prince Dharmapal appeared in her dream and told her his whole sad story. He said to her, 'Tomorrow, you must go to the ghat again and prepare a statue of me with cow dung. Then, when you put my heart into the statue, I will come to life.'

The next morning the woman did as she was told and Prince Dharmapal came back to life. The news of the miraculous resurrection on the river side spread like wildfire. The woman took the prince home where he told her again about his tragic story.

A few days later, Prince Dharmapal went back to the ogre's mansion. He found the ogre sleeping soundly. He decapitated it with one blow of his sword. In another room in the mansion, the princess was sitting in shock, unable to comprehend the fate that had befallen her. When she saw her husband enter, she rushed to him, ecstatic to see him alive. But he pushed her away, saying, 'You betrayed me, wife. After all the dangers I faced to cure your aches and pains, you poisoned me. The only fit fate for you is death.' And, unheeding of the princess' protests, Prince Dharmapal beheaded his wife. At that very moment, the spout, and all the other water sources in his kingdom began to give clear, fresh water.

Prince Dharmapal married the woman who had resurrected him and took her to his kingdom as his princess. He soon became king and ruled his kingdom ably till the end of his days.

Prince Dikpal and the Yogi

A king, rich, famous and powerful, once ruled a large kingdom. He had everything but the lack of a male heir clouded his happiness. He did everything, sought all possible divine interventions, but the royal couple could not have a child. The king finally resigned himself to his fate and prepared to die heir-less.

One day, a *yogi* arrived at the palace begging for alms. The king asked the queen to give the yogi whatever he wanted with her own two hands; perhaps his blessing would give him an heir. But the yogi turned angrily to the king and said, 'Your Highness, it is inauspicious for me to even think of taking alms from a barren woman.' The queen was stung and began to weep. The yogi appeared to relent somewhat and said to the queen, 'Don't weep, your Highness, tell me what the problem is.'

The story came tumbling out: all the fruitless penances, the visits to pilgrimage sites, the hundred different potions and medicines. Dismissing all these cures as bogus, the yogi produced a small packet. He said, 'Your Highness, exactly

a week after you eat this, you will conceive a male child. But, I have one condition: when the prince turns sixteen, you must hand him over to me.'

The king and the queen were ecstatic at the thought of an heir. They scarcely gave the yogi's condition any thought; they would cross the bridge when they came to it. The queen, as predicted, became pregnant within a week of taking the medicine and the entire royal family—along with the whole kingdom—rejoiced.

The prince, Dikpal, grew up quickly. The king invited many gurus of renown to teach him and in no time, Prince Dikpal became adept at many different arts. He became a fine young man and the royal couple was very happy with their son. In all this, they forgot the promise they had made the yogi.

On Prince Dikpal's sixteenth birthday, the yogi turned up at the palace to claim what was rightfully his. The couple, especially the queen, was shocked. They had stopped thinking about their pledge and it was unthinkable that they should part with their son.

The king summoned his minister for advice. The minister said, 'Your Highness, we can always give the yogi another boy. How will he know the difference he hasn't seen the boy?' The king was thrilled with this idea. He had a sixteen-year-old boy brought secretly to the palace, and handed him over to the yogi; he had given strict instructions to the boy to never divulge the secret.

The yogi was shrewd. He wanted to test the king's honesty so he told the boy, 'We are going to my hut, o prince, which is on the other side of this jungle. Two roads go there: one is long but safe, the other is quick but extremely dangerous. Which road should we take?'

The boy promptly replied, 'The longer, safer route, obviously.'

The yogi understood he had been conned: a prince would never have taken such a cowardly stand. He went straight to the king and confronted him. He told the king that if he did not keep his end of the bargain, he would curse seven generations of the king's descendants. The king had no option but to hand his son over.

The yogi still suspected the king and asked Prince Dikpal the same question. The prince told him that despite the danger, the two must take the shorter route. The yogi was convinced and he took Prince Dikpal to his *kuti*, hut.

The yogi told Prince Dikpal that he was to be his disciple; he would bring flowers for the yogi's morning pooja and he would cook for both of them but he must never enter the temple. The yogi would tell Prince Dikpal when the time was right for him to come into the goddess Kali's— whose ardent devotee the yogi was—presence.

The next morning the prince woke up early, took a bath and fetched flowers for the yogi. The yogi entered the temple, carefully locking the door behind him. Dikpal then cooked breakfast and when the yogi finished his prayers, the two ate. After breakfast, the yogi left to beg for alms. The prince was alone now. He thought about his family, his friends and the games he played with them and became sad. He soon got bored of sitting at home and went out into the jungle and returned just before sundown. The yogi arrived in the evening, talked with the prince for a while, ate and went to sleep. The prince went to sleep a little later, after doing the dishes. As time passed, the prince became curious about the yogi's secret pooja. He decided to investigate. One day, when the yogi had left, the prince found the key to the temple and entered it. Inside, there was a huge statue of the goddess Kali, her four hands held various weapons and her outstretched tongue proclaimed her most fearsome aspect. On the wall to the right hung seven human heads.

Even as Prince Dikpal looked on, the heads sniggered. The prince was taken aback. He hesitantly asked the severed heads why they were sniggering. They replied, 'Prince, you have arrived to give us company. Soon, you will join us on this wall.'

The prince didn't understand. He asked, 'Why do you say that? And how do you know that I am a prince?'

One of the heads spoke up, 'We, too, are princes. The yogi tricked our parents, too. With you, the yogi comes to the end of his penance. When he sacrifices eight princes, the goddess Kali will appear to him and grant him the boon of immortality.'

Prince Dikpal replied, in surprise, 'Is that so? And how does one go about stopping this yogi?'

The severed head continued speaking, 'The yogi will ask you to prostrate in front of the idol; which is when he will cut your head off. You should ask him to show you how to do it and when he is lying on the ground, you should cut his head off. Then, sprinkle some of the blood on us and we will come to life, whole again.' The prince agreed and stepped out of the temple, carefully shutting the door behind him.

Some days later, when Prince Dikpal came back with the flowers, he found the yogi waiting for him. The yogi said, 'Son, the time has come for you to enter the goddess' presence.'

He took the prince inside the temple. A curtain covered the severed heads of the dead princes. After an elaborate pooja, the yogi instructed Prince Dikpal to lie face down in front of the idol. Dikpal feigned ignorance and asked the yogi to show him how. When the yogi lay on the floor, the prince quickly cut his head off. He then drew the curtain open and sprinkled some of the blood on the torso-less heads. The dead princes immediately sprang to life. Thanking Dikpal profusely, all the seven princes left for their kingdoms.

Dikpal, however, decided to travel for some time before going home. He travelled extensively in many kingdoms. One day he arrived in a beautiful country with a huge, magnificent palace, hoping to find some days of rest there. As he approached the palace, it appeared deserted. Even as he entered the palace, he could see no one. He came to a royal bedroom. Inside, on a golden bed, lay a beautiful girl. She appeared to be sleeping but he could not see her breathe. He went up to her and felt her pulse, and it was, surprisingly, strong. Prince Dikpal looked around and saw a wand lying next to the bed. He picked it up and experimentally swished it over the girl's head. She came to life.

When asked, the girl said that she was indeed the princess of the kingdom. A band of demons had killed off all the subjects of the kingdom and her parents, and had taken over the palace. However, one old demon had taken a fancy to the princess and had kept her alive. In the morning, all the demons would go out to find food, and the old demon, to keep her imprisoned, would put her to sleep with the magic wand. She then became frantic, and implored Dikpal to go away before the demons came back. But Dikpal was enthralled with this beautiful princess and her tragic story. He kept sitting by her side. When they heard the demons arrive, the prince put the princess back to sleep and quickly made his exit. The old demon came into the room, woke the princess up and spoke to her for some time. Soon, he left, after putting the princess to sleep again. Prince Dikpal crept out of hiding and spent the night talking to the princess.

As time passed, it became clear to Dikpal that things could not carry on this way. He was bound to be caught by the demons some day or the other. Dikpal knew that the demons were bound to have some secret to their vitality. He urged the princess to find out what it was. That night, the old demon entered the bedchamber and woke up the princess who pretended to be very sad. The demon asked her what the matter was.

She said, 'You killed my parents and left me an orphan. Now, for better or for worse, you are the only one left in my life. And if you die, the other demons will kill me. If I feel like this, how can I be happy?'

The old demon laughed, 'We demons cannot be killed easily and you needn't be worried about being alone, child.'

'But you must have some weak point, some way you die, what is it?'

'But, child, I cannot tell you that!'

'Please, you must, the knowledge will make me feel safer.'

'All right, if you must know, there is a pond to the east, about one mile from here. We demons draw all our strength from that pond. But, in the pond, is a hollow pole. There are three bumblebees inside. If anyone can cleanly break the pole, the bumblebees will fly out. One will shoot up towards the sky; the other will burrow underground—these two cannot be caught. The third, if caught, must be wiped out in such a manner that no blood spills to the ground. If this is done, all the demons will die out.'

The princess, seemingly happy, said, 'I am glad that it is so difficult to kill you. I feel much safer.' Dikpal, who had all along been listening in on the conversation, set out the next morning.

Soon, he came to the pond. Prince Dikpal prayed to the gods and waded into the pond. In the middle, the pole stood. Dikpal swung his *gada*, mace, and the pole broke into two pieces. As predicted, two bumblebees escaped but he managed to catch the third. As soon as he crushed the bee, the demons all fell dead, right in the middle of whatever they were doing.

He then went back to the palace, rescued the princess, and went back to his kingdom where he was welcomed with open arms.

Dhon Cholecha, the Miracle Ewe

Pankhu Maicha was an only child and her parents doted on her. The only responsibility she had was to ensure the well-being of her pet ewe, which she had named Dhon Cholecha. In the absence of a sibling or a playmate, Dhon Cholecha was Pankhu's only companion.

The smooth course of Pankhu's life was suddenly severely interrupted by her mother's death. Her father, thinking that Pankhu would need a mother, remarried. However, her stepmother hated Pankhu. In the daytime, when her father was not around, she was made to do most of the housework and was never given enough to eat. Pankhu was miserable and spent most nights weeping, thinking of her mother who loved her dearly.

Matters went from bad to worse when a daughter was born to Pankhu's stepmother. She now had to do all the housework and received only scraps from the table to eat. Her father, too, infatuated with his new wife and the novelty of a new daughter, began to neglect her. Now, the only support she had in her life was her pet sheep.

As time passed, both Pankhu and her stepsister grew up into lovely young girls; Pankhu, especially, grew up to be a radiant adolescent. Her good health began to bother her stepmother greatly: she was, after all, doing everything she could to destroy it. The stepmother noticed that Pankhu looked especially happy and at peace after her daily outings with Dhon Cholecha whom she took out to graze. One day, she asked her daughter, Pankhu's stepsister, to follow Pankhu to the pasture where she took the sheep out. The stepsister followed Pankhu and hid behind a tree. Soon, she saw a strange and wondrous sight. Dhon Cholecha regurgitated something on a plate that Pankhu had woven out of leaves and Pankhu began to eat it. Fascinated and disgusted, the stepsister was unable to contain her curiosity. She ran out, frantically calling to Pankhu. 'What are you eating?'

Pankhu looked up, as if expecting this intrusion, and replied, simply, 'I'm eating *kholay*, porridge, do you want some?'

Seeing Pankhu eat the kholay with such obvious relish, her step-sister nodded. Pankhu invited her to sit down and when her stepsister tasted the porridge, she found that it was indeed very delicious. Pankhu Maicha was worried, and made her sister promise that she would never tell

---

Dhon Cholecha, the Miracle Ewe

mother and father about Dhon Cholecha. But that evening, when mother asked, Pankhu's stepsister told her everything about Dhon Cholecha, the miraculous ewe.

Stepmother became very jealous on hearing about the miraculous ewe which favoured her stepdaughter so much. That evening, she told father, 'It's been days since we ate meat and I am beginning to feel weak; please slaughter the ewe tomorrow. In any case, she's useless: she neither produces good wool nor lambs.' Father agreed. Pankhu overheard the conversation and became very sad. The next morning, when she took Dhon Cholecha out to graze, she told her everything and began weeping. But Dhon Cholecha only said, 'Worry not, Pankhu, I was expecting this day; a sheep, sooner or later, must be served up at the table. When they finish eating me, gather up all my bones and bury them in one place. In a couple of weeks, a tree will take root on the spot which will produce as many *yomaries* as you can eat.'

That evening father slaughtered the ewe. The whole family feasted. Stepmother cruelly offered some mutton curry and rice to Pankhu but she refused to even come out of her room. Later, she collected all the bones and buried them in a nearby field. Soon enough, a huge tree grew on the spot and began giving yomaries. Excited, Pankhu climbed up the tree and began eating the delicious, juicy sweets. Soon, two men came along and seeing Pankhu eat the yomaries with such obvious relish, asked for some. She threw some down but the men could not catch the sweets. They asked her to climb down with some. When Pankhu handed over the yomari, the men grabbed her and quickly took her home. They figured that if she could grow yomari on trees, she must certainly be able to perform all sorts of miracles. They put her to work preparing another type of sweet, *jatamari*, and went out.

As the delicious smell of jatamari filled the air, a rat came out of its hole and told Pankhu, 'If you give me some of the jatamari, I will tell you a secret.' Pankhu fed the rat and it told her, 'The two men who brought you here are actually ghosts. After eating the jatamari, they will kill you. If you want to escape, you must do so now. On your way out, spit on the doorstep and mark it with charcoal so they cannot follow you. These ghosts have collected much gold; you may take as much as you want on your way out. Now, you must leave.' Pankhu filled a bag with jewels and precious stones, spat on the doorstep and marked it with charcoal, and left.

Dhon Cholecha, the Miracle Ewe

Pankhu's family had already retired for the night when she reached home. She knocked at the door, but she got no response. She called out to her father but still no one came to the door. Pankhu then shouted that she couldn't stand outside forever carrying this heavy load. Stepmother began to wonder what Pankhu might have brought and soon opened the door and let her in. Seeing the sack full of jewels, she asked Pankhu where she got them from. Pankhu told her.

Greedy beyond belief, stepmother told her daughter to go to the yomari tree and do exactly as Pankhu had done. Her daughter climbed the tree and soon enough, the ghosts came and tricked her into making jatamari. The rat came out and asked the girl for a taste but she was engrossed in her work. She swatted at the rat with her ladle and it instantly died. Then she collected all the jewels she could carry and began walking home, not knowing that she needed to spit on the doorstep and mark it with charcoal. The ghosts found that they had been tricked and they easily tracked her. Catching up with her near the yomari tree, they killed her and hung her remains from the branches.

Stepmother waited impatiently till evening and then went up the road to find her daughter. When she came to the yomari tree, she saw her daughter's remains hanging from a branch. She began weeping, cursing herself for being greedy. Father, too, wept and blamed stepmother for her daughter's death. He realized how wrong his attitude towards his daughter had been and from then on, showered her with all his love.

Dhon Cholecha, the Miracle Ewe

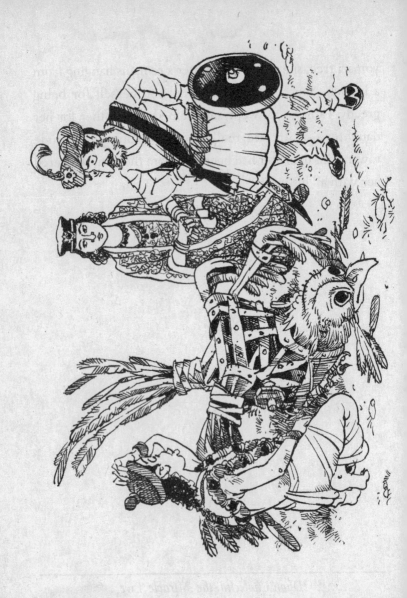

The Fake Vishnu

A handsome young man was once in love with the princess of his kingdom. But he was poor and could not possibly ask the king for his daughter's hand in marriage. Yet he could not stop thinking about her and became obsessed with ways to win the princess over.

He knew that the *ista devta*, guardian god, of the royal household was Vishnu. An idea came to him and he immediately acted upon it. He built a mechanized version of *Garud*, the bird that Vishnu uses for transportation, coloured his face and body blue, attached two additional arms to his torso and flew to the princess' window.

Inside, he saw the princess sitting on her bed, crying. He climbed into her room. The princess was overjoyed; she fell at his feet, fervently exclaiming, 'Thank you, Lord, for answering my prayers so quickly.'

The fake Vishnu asked the princess, 'I know you are in great distress, princess, which is why I came. Tell me, what is your problem?'

The princess told him the whole story. A neighbouring

kingdom was very powerful and the king had written to her father expressing a desire to add her to his harem. If her father refused, he would surely attack and annex all their land. But she did not want to marry the king for he was cruel and his harem was very large: she would only be a minor wife.

The young man reassured the princess, 'Have no fear, princess, for I, Vishnu, will fight on your father's side, and there is no way he will lose.'

The princess told the fake Vishnu that her father would only believe her if he told him this in person. Afraid that he would be caught, the fake Vishnu told the princess that her father's devotion was yet to be tested. He would tell the king of his support in case of war, but the king could not see him. She agreed. The fake Vishnu and the princess went to the door of the king's bedchamber and there, Vishnu announced his support. Heartened by this pledge of support, the king drafted a letter for his adversary. He wrote that he was prepared to go to war and would, under no circumstances, give his daughter away to him in marriage.

On the day of the battle, the two armies faced each other on a vast plain. The fake Vishnu hovered over the battlefield.

Even to his untrained eye, he could see that their army was vastly outnumbered by the cruel king's. It would be a rout. He did not know what to do and just simply kept floating above the battlefield.

The real Vishnu was watching the proceedings from heaven. The king and his daughter had always been favourite devotees of his and he wanted them to win. He therefore endowed the young man with such power that he swooped down on to the battlefield and vanquished the more powerful army with ease. However, as soon as he had routed the army, Lord Vishnu took away all the young man's powers and he crashed to the ground.

The princess and the king rushed to the fallen garud, shocked that this Vishnu was, in fact, fake. However, they realized that he had always been at their side and had destroyed their enemies. In gratitude, the king gave the young man his daughter in marriage as well as half his kingdom.

The Fake Vishnu

Why Yetis Don't Like Pine Forests

A man had his farm high up on a mountain. The earth was hard and stony and there was very little water. Life was difficult; the farmer toiled hard but received very little for his efforts.

One afternoon, the farmer came back home for lunch. He had been working since early morning and he was tired and hungry. His wife, however, told him that she had prepared no food because there was nothing to prepare it with. The farmer quietly turned around and went to the small water mill he had constructed on the rivulet that ran close to their house to grind some corn. As he waited for the mill to do its work, he fell asleep. When he woke up, it was dusk. It was beginning to be cold and only one thought obsessed him: he needed to get warm. He got up, went to the pine forest across the rivulet, gathered as many pine needles and pines as he could carry and lit a fire in the small courtyard outside the mill. He then took some of the old yak butter that was used as grease for the mill and began to massage his tired legs with it. He intended to sit there until some of the tiredness left him.

A yeti, curious, was watching the farmer massage his legs. Unable to contain its curiosity, the yeti sidled up to the farmer and sat on the ground next to him. The farmer, for a minute, was scared out of his wits. But he immediately regained his composure and asked the yeti what it wanted.

The yeti asked him, 'Why are you rubbing your legs?'

The farmer said, 'To soothe them.'

When asked if the yeti could rub its legs too, the farmer agreed. However, rubbing the legs without any lotion would be useless. The yeti would have to use the resin of the pine tree. The yeti immediately jumped up and rushed off into the forest. Some time later, it came back with some resin in a bowl it had made from leaves. It sat down and began rubbing its legs with the resin. However, the resin was sticky and the yeti began panicking as its fingers began to stick. The farmer told him that this was happening because the resin had not melted well; it must move closer to the fire for the resin to melt. The yeti moved closer and the flammable resin soon caught fire. It ran towards the forest where its friends were waiting. The friends asked what had happened, but the unbearable pain had made the yeti incoherent. It could only scream, 'Pine resin, pine forest . . .' at intervals before dying. The other yetis assumed that something in the pine forest had killed their friend. They fled the area and since then, one can never find yetis in pine forests.

Why Yetis Don't Like Pine Forests

Desire

Gonu was a woodcutter who made his living selling wood in the city. One day, Gopu came to Gonu's village from the city to observe and experience village life. He walked around the village, speaking to the people and asking them about their lives. In the evening, he started on his way back to the city. He was very tired from his trip and did not want to walk. He soon came across Gonu who was going to the city on his buffalo cart to be on time for the morning market. Gopu asked Gonu if he could hitch a ride with him on the cart. Gonu agreed and when they reached the city, Gopu helped Gonu sell the wood. The two became friends and whenever Gonu went to the city thereafter, Gopu helped him sell his wood.

One Purnima, the night when the moon is full, Gonu had come to the city to sell wood. It so happened that every Purnima, the king of the land would have his chefs prepare eighty-four delicacies and he would eat them out of utensils of gold in full view of his subjects. Gonu wanted to see this spectacle and stayed back with Gopu to watch. That night, after dinner, the two friends went to the palace grounds where a large crowd had gathered. The attendants had set up a huge dining table that was groaning under the weight of the eighty-four dishes. The moon was shining brightly and the gold utensils glowed dully. Presently, the king came out and ate his dinner while his subjects looked on, their mouths watering. On their way back from the palace, Gonu said to Gopu, 'Friend, that was quite a spectacle. I cannot stop thinking about it. How dearly I wish to eat all those delicacies the king was eating; I really wouldn't mind even the leftovers.'

Gopu looked at his friend, aghast. He told Gonu that even to think such a thing was a sin. If the palace got so much as a whiff of such a preposterous idea, the two could lose their heads. But Gonu insisted, begged and cajoled Gopu till he finally said, 'All right, Gonu, I have a friend in the palace kitchen. Perhaps I could prevail upon him to give you a taste of some food from the royal plates before they throw the food away.' When Gopu broached this subject with his friend in the kitchen, he looked at the two as though they had gone mad. He initially refused outright, but when they continued pleading with him, he decided to let Gonu have a taste, provided the king knew of the plan. Gonu had no option but to agree. Gopu's friend also made them agree that if the king became angry, the entire blame would have to be shouldered by the two.

The three went into the royal presence. The king heard Gonu out as he tremblingly made his request. Surprisingly, the king did not get angry. He heard Gonu out and made a proposal: if Gonu worked in the king's fields for three years, he could, at the end of the three years have the entire eighty-four dishes—not leftovers—on the king's gold plates, on Purnima.

Gonu worked in the fields with a will and the king's fields yielded more than ever before. The king was impressed by Gonu's single-minded devotion, but did not say anything. At the end of the three years, which passed soon enough, the day arrived when Gonu would eat the king's feast. On Purnima, the attendants set up the table and the dishes. But the man who sat down to eat was not the king. The crowd started buzzing with whispers.

But when Gonu sat down to eat, he saw a yogi looking hungrily at him. He invited the yogi to the table and shared his meal with him. The king saw all this and was exceedingly happy: not only was Gonu hard working, he was also a kind man. After the meal, the king proudly announced to everyone present that Gonu was to be his new prime minister.